Microcomputers in civil engineering

Microcomputers in civil engineering

Trevor Bell and Roger Plank

Construction Press
London and New York

0598847X

George Godwin
an imprint of:
Longman Group Limited
Longman House, Burnt Mill, Harlow
Essex CM20 2JE, England
Associated companies throughout the world

Published in the United States of America
by Longman Inc., New York

© George Godwin, 1985

All rights reserved; no part of this publication may be reproduced, stored in a retrieval system, or transmitted in any form or by any means, electronic, mechanical, photocopying, recording, or otherwise, without the prior written permission of the Publishers.

First published 1985

British Library Cataloguing In Publication Data
Bell, Trevor
Micro-computers in civil engineering
1. Civil engineering — Data processing
2. Microcomputers
I. Title II. Plank, Roger
624'.028'5404 TA345

ISBN 0-86095-883-3

Library of Congress Cataloguing in Publication Data
Bell, Trevor, 1946-
Micro-computers in civil engineering.
Bibliography: p.
Includes index.
1. Civil engineering – Data processing. 2. Micro-computers. I. Plank, Roger, 1949- . II. Title.
III. Title: Microcomputers in civil engineering.
TA345.B43 1984 624'.028'54 84-17053
ISBN 0-86095-883-3

Printed in Great Britain by Pitman Press, Bath

D
624.0285'4
BEL

Contents

Preface

It has taken us over three years to write this book. The time taken is neither a reflection of the complexity of the subject nor our lassitude in producing it. The reason is that we have tried to keep abreast of the rapidly changing microcomputer technology and its implications for the civil engineer. Although apparently better and cheaper computers are being announced almost weekly, we have decided to finalise the text in the full knowledge that, by the time it is published, parts of it may be out of date. However, a significant part of this book is, we believe, ageless; we discuss in detail the way in which microcomputers should be used in day-to-day civil and structural engineering design and we would argue that this is almost independent of the hardware itself.

While our interpretation of the technical intricacies of computers may not be as detailed as that available in many other microcomputer books, we are civil engineers, not computer scientists. We believe that, as such, we are in a better position to advise other civil engineers and to span the two disciplines. There are few other texts which cover this subject, and our experience of running mid-career courses for practising engineers suggests a need for this book. The book is, in fact, based on the experience not only of the authors but also of their colleagues who have been actively involved in developing the ideas presented. In particular, we would like to acknowledge the invaluable contributions of Ian Burgess and Clive Emberey of Sheffield University.

WTB
RJP

Sheffield, July 1984

Preface

Chapter 1

Introduction

Computers have been used in civil and structural engineering for many years and are recognised as an important tool for certain applications. As computing costs fall so usage increases; between 1960 and 1977 the cost of a large computer (often referred to as a 'mainframe' computer) divided by its computing power had fallen by a factor of over 100 (Terman, 1977) and, as we are well aware, is still falling. However, both capital and recurrent costs of larger computers are such that it is still not generally economic to use them for relatively routine analysis and design work. The advances in technology which resulted in more powerful and cheaper large computers have had an even more dramatic effect on small computers and it is the use of such systems – microcomputers, or micros as they are often known – that we shall be dealing with in this book.

Of course small computers are not new in civil engineering. During the 1970s a few desk-top computer systems were marketed with reasonable success, partly because the supplier was able to offer a range of suitable programs in addition to the hardware. This idea of a 'turnkey' system (in which the computer and the programs are sold as a unit) was popular because it enabled a purchaser to treat the system as a black box, requiring no specialised knowledge of computers and simplifying the transition to computerisation. However, because there was only a small number of firms offering this service and the number of sales was limited, costs of the desk-top systems were still relatively high.

During the latter half of the 1970s a number of so-called microcomputers appeared on the market. The marketing policy for these was quite different from that for the earlier desk-top systems, being aimed initially at the enthusiast or hobbyist. The specification and power of even the earliest of these microcomputers were, in many cases, comparable with those of the more expensive desk-top systems. However, because they are not generally sold as turnkey systems, successful implementation is more difficult although the potential advantages are considerable. Certainly difficulties (real or imagined) have been experienced, including hardware reliability, after-sales back-up, and lack of standardisation for both hardware and programs. Many of these problems are now being resolved and microcomputers no longer justify the early criticisms which were levelled at them. Modern micros are cheap, reliable and their increasing power enables them to be used in ever wider applications. In this book we shall be studying the ways in which micros might most effectively be used in civil engineering offices, concentrating largely on design.

A historical perspective of computing in civil engineering should not, of course, deal only with computers but also with the way in which they are used. A number of civil engineering firms, particularly small ones, saw the development of small computers as a relatively cheap way of providing an in-house facility, often in place of bureau services. It is therefore not surprising that early computer-aided design programs were largely smaller versions of traditional mainframe packages, for instance plane frame analysis. However, it is not only cost which has made small computers so popular. Many users have felt more at ease with a small device connected to the outside world by nothing more than an electricity plug. Furthermore, because they are intended for use by one individual in a fairly narrowly defined way (i.e. they are 'dedicated', 'stand-alone' systems), no complex and apparently meaningless commands are required to operate them – they are 'user friendly'. However, user friendliness is not a function of the hardware alone and program writers soon became aware of the need to design programs which were easy to use. Unfortunately, in doing so, full advantage was often taken of the characteristics peculiar to one specific make of microcomputer. Problems of machine dependency, in which a program developed for one particular microcomputer could not immediately run on a different machine (and in some cases the effort of conversion was as great as the program development itself), were aggravated. With developments in programs lagging behind those in hardware, the problem of obsolescence also began to appear. Some systems purchased in the hope or expectancy of a wider range of programs becoming available in the future might be seen in retrospect as a poor investment. Although the hardware and existing programs may be perfectly satisfactory, some micros which were very popular in the early days are now having very little in the way of new programs being developed on them.

Fortunately a degree of stability has been achieved. Gradually a shake-out of the industry has taken place, and certain aspects of microcomputer systems have been generally accepted as a suitable standard. There has also been a realisation by some program writers that portability of software (as far as is reasonably possible) enabling easy transfer to different micros is desirable. Despite continuing developments in hardware and an increasing number of manufacturers making even greater claims for their latest hardware, there is now a sufficiently strong user-population to ensure that these current standards are not made obsolete overnight.

In fact the problems of obsolescence concern more the software than the hardware. Microcomputer manufacturers have realised that a potential buyer will often require a complete working system including hardware and software. Whether these are sold as a package (like the desk-top systems) or independently is of little importance, compared to immediate availablility. The latest and best micro is of no use without suitable programs to run on it. Unfortunately program development, particularly in a specialist area such as civil engineering, can be a lengthy process. Program writers cannot therefore hope to adapt their programs continually to suit the whims of hardware manufacturers as the latest computer rolls off the production line.

Recognising this, most manufacturers provide a facility enabling programs written to accepted standards to run (in principle at least) on new models.

The hardware and the form in which the software is developed have therefore been through a period of rapid evolution, and although we can expect technical developments to continue apace, the implications for a user in the short term should not be too great.

But what of the software itself? The initial rush to convert programs from bigger computers was part of the vision that micros were simply a very cheap way of introducing traditional computing into design offices. This was followed by a realisation that 'user friendliness' does not depend only on the hardware and many of the traditional mainframe applications were given a new treatment. (It is interesting to note that in parallel with these developments, larger computer systems were also becoming more user friendly with input and output via terminals rather than more traditional and cumbersome methods, and similar improvements were being made to the programs themselves.) However, it is only relatively recently that micros have begun to be viewed not as an alternative to mainframes but, because of the ease with which communication can be effected between man and machine, as a tool rather more suited to much of the routine design work of civil engineering. In this respect they can be seen more in terms of the evolution of the programmable calculator although they are not only more powerful but are also more convenient to use. We are now beginning to see a much wider range of programs for relatively routine work and these are fundamentally different in concept and approach from many of the more traditional programs. It therefore seems an appropriate time to write this book to appraise and learn from our experiences in this period of very rapid development and to look at how microcomputers can best be used in civil and structural engineering. Despite the exposure which many of us now have to micros there is still a lack of understanding as to what they can do and how they might best be used. We shall therefore try to present a rational view of their potential role in design offices in particular, highlighting the possible advantages and pointing out some of the potential problems. Before examining how this potential can best be realised we shall describe briefly (without detailed electronics) how a micro functions and give an introduction to computer languages and programming. Although it is not necessary for an engineer to have any detailed knowledge of the hardware we feel that it is important to have some understanding of the principles involved, first to assess and identify possible applications, and second to appreciate that computers are, in fact, very simple machines. The nature of the civil engineering industry is such that no comprehensive list of suitable and unsuitable uses can be given; indeed, every organisation will have its own peculiar requirements. Knowing the general capabilities of microcomputers should enable individuals to assess the potential role of micros in their organisation without needing a detailed understanding of how the computer works. It is also helpful when discussing requirements with salesmen to be able to understand, and even parry, jargon. The treatment given in Chapter 3 in describing the internal workings of a microcomputer is intentionally simple. The physical components of a microcomputer system are described and typical requirements for civil engineering are discussed, for instance, in terms of alternative printers which are available and the various mass storage devices which can be used. The function of each of the components, as well as the relative advantages of different alternatives, are also discussed.

Similarly, there is no need for engineers to be conversant with programming techniques and a good program should be capable of being used by an engineer without any knowledge of programming. Nevertheless, there are many simple tasks which are highly suitable for treatment using a micro, but for which no commercial programs are available. Some engineers will therefore wish to develop their own programs, while others will be content to use the micro in a similar sense to the way in which calculators are currently used. For the former there are many other texts which deal specifically with programming; but again, in order to discuss in greater detail the potential role for micros in civil engineering, a brief introduction is given to system software, particularly operating systems, in Chapter 4, and to BASIC, the most common programming language on microcomputers, in Chapter 5. A fundamental understanding of programming will also aid general awareness and enable a more educated use of programs.

We have attempted to present a guide as to what characterises good quality software, whether self-written or purchased commercially, in a little more detail in Chapter 6. Although not an exhaustive guide, it will provide a useful basis both for assessing possible programs before purchase and for developing programs in-house.

The general use of mass storage in the form of disc files is given in Chapter 7. Again micros can be used without a detailed knowledge of file systems, but some background can be invaluable in assessing potential applications and comparing different systems.

In Chapter 8 some advice is given as to how various features can be incorporated within programs in order to produce high-quality software capable of being used easily by others and even of being marketed commercially. The ideas should be valuable to program writers, and a number of examples are included to illustrate the different techniques described.

The use of database systems is described in Chapter 9. Although many of the applications of databases are not directly concerned with design, they can be a very powerful tool for the civil engineer and their use is likely to increase rapidly as their advantages are recognised. Again examples are used to illustrate the techniques involved.

Finally some guidance is given in Chapter 10 on setting up a system. Because of the diversity of the civil engineering profession, selecting a system – like the design process itself – cannot follow a preset formula. We have therefore suggested points which may need to be examined and have attempted to identify possible problems.

What we shall not be doing is presenting a detailed account of the electronic workings of a microcomputer or of sophisticated programming – there is a large number of specialised texts which cover these subjects. We shall be concerned almost exclusively with the use of micros in design; their use for draughting or as control devices will not be discussed in any detail.

In writing this book we have been acutely aware of the language barrier which seems to have grown around microcomputer enthusiasts. Jargon is an unfortunate necessity in any specialist subject and computing is no exception. Whilst some use of jargon would appear to shield ignorance, its essential role is to act as a form of shorthand. We shall endeavour to avoid its unnecessary use and explain in simple terms the meaning of some of the more common examples. In doing so we hope to dispel the apparent complexity which much of the jargon creates and for reference a glossary of terms is included.

Although comparisons will be made, where appropriate, with other devices, notably larger computers, we shall be focusing exclusively on microcomputers. We hope that the book, which is based on many years of experience, will serve many purposes. For those who already have a microcomputer it should enable more effective use of the system and perhaps identify ways in which the system itself could be improved. It should also enable individuals or organisations who are contemplating the purchase of a system to assess the potential and approach the implementation in a sound and rational manner. For the program writer the advice on programming techniques should be most valuable, and for the engineer who simply wishes to keep abreast of developments in this area or who wants to be able to understand the enthusiasm of his younger colleagues, it will hopefully prove a readable and explanatory text.

Chapter 2

Computer-aided design

It is in design calculations rather than in automated draughting that the civil engineering profession is likely to see the greatest use of microcomputers. We shall be using the term 'computer-aided design' (CAD) in perhaps a looser sense than is often implied. In manufacturing industries, CAD might typically involve the optimisation of a component to be mass produced, whilst in the electronics field it might refer to the design of integrated circuits. In either case it normally culminates in the automated production of working drawings, and may be integrated with a computer-aided manufacturing process (CAM).

The structure of the civil engineering profession and the nature of civil engineering design techniques are generally not well-suited to this treatment. Seldom are the designer and constructor the same engineer or even part of the same organisation. Therefore there is not only less incentive to achieve the absolute 'optimum' solution, but also great difficulty in quantifying costs accurately. Similarly, without mass production runs, the cost of optimising the design cannot be offset against a number of projects, and the 'one-off' nature of projects makes it difficult to automate the draughting. Civil engineering designers, working according to Codes of Practice, forced to make imprecise assumptions about loading data and needing to incorporate significant factors of safety because of the serious consequences of a failure, are therefore unable to make use of computer-aided design techniques in the same way that engineers in other disciplines have done. Nevertheless, the time spent by designers on formal calculations and in producing presentation calculations suggests that computers may offer some benefits. In this chapter we shall therefore be studying the role that microcomputers in particular might have in the routine design work of a civil engineer. In doing so we shall be considering the microcomputer largely as a calculating device, and excluding other possible applications such as control devices on the construction site.

2.1 The strengths of computers

It is important to remember that a computer is not able to do anything which could not be done by manual calculation. Indeed, it works in a very pedestrian way, calculating for instance the product of two numbers by a series of additions! This is in fact similar to the way in which an electronic calculator functions, combining simple operations to enable the determination of more advanced mathematical functions, and is discussed in further detail in Chapter 3. A computer, however, extends this concept and allows a sequence of mathematical operations to be undertaken with intermediate values stored within its memory. It is only because it is able to carry out these operations accurately and extremely quickly, and has this powerful memory facility that the computer is such a useful tool. It is therefore worth studying the implications of these three characteristics, namely accuracy, memory and speed, in a little more detail.

2.1.1 Accuracy

The computer may be able to provide greater accuracy in a number of ways – through the use of more rigorous methods, by virtue of its precision in calculating to a large number of significant figures, or simply as a result of its reliability. In many applications the benefit of greater accuracy is not apparent but in certain cases one or more of these considerations may be important.

The process of design in civil and structural engineering is generally one in which a complicated pattern of behaviour is represented to some degree of approximation by a mathematical model. The level of approximation is reflected partly in the need for factors of safety, and in many cases may lead to over-conservative designs. One advantage of using computer-aided design might be that we can use more accurate mathematical models and hence achieve more efficient solutions. Whilst this may be true for some types of problem – a finite element analysis is no doubt invaluable in the design of offshore oil platforms or box girder bridges – the designer of more modest works is less able to take advantage of such accurate methods. This may be for a number of reasons, including:

(a) the uncertainty of loadings;

(b) the variation of material properties;

(c) the fact that design rules and methods are often based, at least in part, on experience rather than rigorous analytical techniques;

(d) the need in any case for some degree of idealisation.

The advantage to be gained from a more accurate analysis may therefore be limited, although there are examples, such as the design of a space frame, where, within sensible constraints of time and economy, the only realistic method of solution is by using a computer.

Of course, this is not the only way in which computer-aided design may contribute to a more accurate solution. A microcomputer will typically work to an accuracy of seven significant figures but, although in some applications such accuracy is necessary, this precision may not always be important to an engineer who is working with imposed loads specified to the nearest 0.5 kN/m^2. Indeed, the most important contribution which computers make in terms of accuracy is probably through their ability to maintain their precision when the human brain might otherwise become tired, distracted or bored. A great deal of detail design and analysis is repetitive in nature – determining bending moments in the members of a frame for a number of load cases, designing the beams and columns (often in itself a repetitive process) for such a frame, and so on. This type of work is often tedious and unrewarding, and the majority of engineers would surely welcome the relief which computers might provide in this respect.

Associated with this advantage is the fact that any revisions in the design can be processed very quickly and easily. There can be nothing more depressing than, on completing a design, being told that the client has requested one or two 'minor amendments' which in the event require the work to be redesigned from the beginning! Whilst the computer does not make such news welcome, it can certainly relieve the designer of much of the anguish he may feel under these circumstances.

In terms of accuracy, then, it would seem that the computer's main advantage is associated with reliability rather than any inherent precision, particularly for routine design work.

2.1.2 Memory

As mentioned above, the computer's memory enables a sequence of calculations, which would require individual treatment using a calculator, to be executed automatically, thereby reducing calculation time. In this sense the memory is contributing to the speed of processing, and there are further ways in which similar benefits may be realised. For instance, the designer using a calculator may often be required to refer to design charts and tables, which have been developed for the convenience of manual design. By incorporating such information within the computer, continual reference to manuals is avoided, with a further increase in efficiency. Moreover, because charts and tables are generally published for discrete values of the variables concerned, interpolation between appropriate figures is normally necessary. Whereas this is a tedious process if done by hand, it is something which can be very easily accommodated within a computer program, and the potential savings in time may be correspondingly increased.

Other advantages offered by the computer's memory include the ability to store the results of specific calculations or to hold large amounts of data, and in this respect the particular use of databases will be discussed in greater detail in Chapter 9. In general, however, the computer's memory is simply contributing to an increase in overall calculation speed compared with conventional techniques.

2.1.3 Speed

Without doubt, the greatest direct advantage to be gained from a computer is the speed with which calculations, or rather a sequence of calculations, can be carried out, and the resulting savings which may be realised in a designer's time. This is not simply a function of the processing speed of the computer; as we have seen above, the computer's memory can make a significant contribution in this respect. The advantage of speed is particularly important where repetitive calculations are involved or where design data can be incorporated within the program.

However, whilst there are many cases in which it is undoubtedly true that calculation time may be dramatically reduced by using a computer, this advantage may be outweighed by the time taken to gain access to the computer or by using an unnecessarily complicated method of solution. Fortunately, access time is only likely to be a problem on a mainframe computer where technical applications can sometimes be classified as low priority jobs and only allowed to run if it is not pay day, maintenance day, file up-date day or on condition that it is not during working hours! However, even on mainframes accessibility is improving and in any case microcomputers should present little difficulty in terms of such delay. The question of over-complicated methods of solution is really in the hands of the designer. A more thorough solution than could be reasonably produced by hand may in itself be desirable, but if a hand calculation is adequate there may be little point in using anything more sophisticated.

Used sensibly, the computer may therefore save design time, particularly with respect to formal calculations, and enable more designs to be processed in the same time, thus increasing productivity and business efficiency. As an indirect benefit, however, this saving in time could be used, for instance, to examine a number of different alternatives, and in civil engineering where there are seldom unique solutions this could result in 'better' designs. Alternatively, a more thorough solution may be obtained without a time penalty compared with simpler manual methods, in some cases providing solutions to problems which could not realistically be achieved using hand calculations.

2.2 The limitations of computers

The computer is clearly a device which can carry out calculations very quickly and accurately, and is able to store data and results within its memory to be accessed as required. However, we have perhaps been mistakenly led to believe that the computer is vastly superior to the human brain and that virtually any problem can be solved by a computer. Whilst there is an element of truth in both of these statements, they suggest some superior ability which is quite misleading. We have already seen that whereas an instruction to multiply two numbers could be carried out mentally by us, the computer can only do this by a series of additions! More important, since a computer can only operate according to prescribed instructions (the program) which must be totally unambiguous, it should be apparent that in some respects the computer is vastly inferior to the human brain. Evidently we should be proud of our mental agility and rightly regard the computer as a tool, albeit a powerful one, to carry out the drudgery of calculations for us.

It would therefore seem that the computer and the human have complementary strengths and it is perhaps useful to identify these before discussing how computers might most effectively be used in design. The qualities of speed, memory and accuracy afforded by a computer were discussed above, and in each of these the computer is potentially more powerful than the human brain. Despite the need to process them in very simple steps, calculations can be carried out much more quickly by computer and, depending on the storage capacity of a particular installation, thousands of numbers and instructions can be easily accommodated within, and immediately recalled from, the computer's memory. The human brain has a wide range of information to remember (much of it subconsciously) including how to control our physical actions and the range of vocabulary which we need as part of our everyday existence: 'spare' memory is correspondingly reduced and our capacity for recalling factual information therefore much more limited than that of the computer.

In terms of accuracy too, although the computer is inherently no more accurate than the human brain, when viewed realistically the time taken for us to execute mathematical calculations to the same degree of accuracy as a computer would in general be unacceptably long. We may therefore conclude that computers are quicker, more accurate and have a superior memory when compared with the human.

The implication which we might draw from this is that the computer can do anything the human brain can do, but it will do it very much more quickly. If this were true then we would indeed have a facility of awesome power. A limitation, however, is the need to specify the program instructions in a completely logical and unambiguous fashion, and this is where the computer is unable to compete with the flexibility of the human brain. Whereas a computer, through the program, is only able to operate according to rigid rules, the human brain is capable of considerable creativity, is able to think in concepts as well as rules, and can think 'laterally'. There are many examples for which it is difficult to program a computer effectively – simple checks on lists of names where variations such as 'John', 'Jon', and 'Johnny' would be regarded as different by the computer whereas they would be recognised as acceptable alternatives by the human brain. Even the game of chess is difficult to treat effectively because of the large number of possible moves and their implications. The human can, however, assess realistic possibilities much better than a computer in this type of situation and, together with our ability to recognise similarities as well as identities, we are better equipped to deal with imperfectly defined problems.

In conclusion, it would appear that computers are very good at carrying out calculations (and indeed making decisions) according to rigid, well-defined rules, and under these circumstances could not only save the designer a great deal of time but also relieve him of much tedious work. On the other hand, they are incapable of 'original thought', and where some degree of creativity or subjectivity is required, they are much less useful. If, however, the human and the computer can be used to complement each other, each performing those tasks for which they are best equipped, a most effective arrangement is likely to be achieved.

2.3 Batch processing and interactive processing

Before we try to assess the potential advantages of using computers in civil engineering, we ought to understand a little about how computers are used. Essentially there are two ways in which a computer can be operated – batch processing and interactive processing – and from the user's point of view these are quite different.

2.3.1 Batch processing

Although in the pioneering days of computers the user had sole access to the machine, it was not long before it became apparent that such usage was inefficient. Large mainframe computer installations are very expensive in terms of both capital investment and running costs. To make such a resource exclusively available to an individual would be very inefficient, particularly when we bear in mind that a computer consists of several different components (as will be described in Chapter 3), and that an individual user may require access to only one of these at any particular time. It would be equivalent to making a whole library available to just one borrower at a time, and quite clearly that would not make economic sense. A system of multi-user processing has therefore evolved in which a number of jobs are processed simultaneously under the control of the 'operating system', and this is traditionally achieved using a system of batch processing. In this the job – including program and data – is completely defined at the outset, and on completion of the run the results are transmitted to the user. Traditionally the job is specified in the form of punched cards, although other forms of input such as paper tape, magnetic disc or tape, and recently the more popular VDU (Visual Display Unit) may also be used. Once the job has been submitted it will be placed in a queue dependent upon its priority, and when space is available it will be loaded into the computer (which it may share with other jobs) for execution. On completion the job is removed and the results are printed, typically on a lineprinter, but other forms of output are available. In this way, not only can the computer be used to its capacity, but also, by fully defining the problem at the outset, there are no delays whilst waiting for data, when the computer would otherwise be lying idle.

From the user's point of view, the way in which the computer system does this is of little importance, except for the implication that the work to be processed must be completely specified before starting, and that the results will only be available on completion of the processing. This means not only that all data must be defined initially, but also that any decisions must be preprogrammed, there being no facility for the user to interrupt the execution in order to modify data, provide additional information, or instruct the computer as to the next sequence of calculations.

For many general applications these are not important limitations. Much of the work which is currently processed by computer involves what might be termed deterministic operations – that is, they start with a complete definition of the problem, follow a step-by-step process (which may in fact be quite complex but which is capable of being specified unambiguously) and finally produce an answer. Many commercial applications are of this type; the production of accounts, payroll, etc. are all ideally suited to such a form of processing. Some technical applications too can be solved in this way, but those who have used such a system will be aware of the drawbacks, such as:

(a) data errors mean re-running the complete program;

(b) there is no provision for modifying or providing additional data during a run – a particular limitation in trial-and-error processes;

(c) although processing time may be very short, turnround (i.e. the time between submitting the problem and receiving the results) may be lengthy because of the queuing and the job's priority. This has, however, improved dramatically in recent years with computers becoming ever more powerful, and with terminals linked directly to the computer, resulting in much faster access;
(d) all decisions must be preprogrammed, and hence control over the design is to some extent given to the programmer.

Furthermore, traditional programs have required the preparation of data according to fixed formats. This necessitates a series of numbers being punched onto cards or entered from a terminal and is very tedious, time-consuming and error-prone. Again, this has improved in recent years with the extensive use of general input formats and more dramatically by using interactive pre- and postprocessors. Nevertheless there are many programs still in use which require this rather inflexible and error-prone form of data input.

Thus although recent developments have gone a long way in overcoming some of the disadvantages traditionally associated with batch processing, the need to preprogram all decisions is, by its very nature, one which cannot be avoided.

2.3.2 Interactive computing

Interactive computing is a form of processing which enables the relative advantages of the human brain and the computer to be used to the full. It is much less efficient than batch processing in terms of the use which is made of the computer because the computer – or part of it in the case of a multi-user system – is set aside for his sole use. This not only means that there is no queue (and hence no waiting for the job to be processed) but also that it is no longer necessary to completely define the problem at the outset. The user can therefore direct the course of the solution, providing additional information and making decisions throughout the run as required.

A typical session of interactive computing would start with the user specifying the program to be used. On the user's command the program will begin to run, and as soon as any input data is required the operation will pause until the required data has been specified. In this way data need only be entered as and when required by the program. Perhaps an even bigger advantage, however, is that the form of data input can be made very simple by displaying a message, referred to as a prompt, indicating the information which is currently required. Compared with the effort needed to prepare data according to fixed formats for batch processing with only a program manual as a guide, this is a considerable advantage.

Apart from specifying input data in this way, it is possible to enter instructions controlling the course of the solution on the basis of results previously calculated. For instance, in the design of a reinforced concrete beam, the amount of reinforcement required may in the user's opinion be excessive, and he could – by giving the appropriate instruction – modify the beam dimensions and recalculate the amount of reinforcement. In a batch processing mode not only must such decisions be built into the program, but some means of automatically modifying the beam dimensions must also be incorporated. This can become clumsy but the only alternative is to end the program, print the results and allow the user to submit modified data for a new run.

Clearly for trial-and-error methods interactive computing offers considerable advantages over batch processing, and these can be summarised as:

(a) instant access and response, providing very quick turnround;
(b) ease of data input and editing, minimising the number of errors and abortive runs which may occur;
(c) control remaining with the user, enabling computers to be used for less well defined problems than can be realistically treated using a batch processing system.

Interactive computing is thus quicker and easier from the user's standpoint and also extends the potential for computer application. The disadvantages are that computers are being used 'less efficiently', and for very long, complicated routines there may be delays in the display of information on the screen while calculations are completed. On a multi-user system these delays may be accentuated in an arbitrary way simply because of the requirements of other users; on a microcomputer, the actual processing speed may be relatively slow, and this may be further reduced if the limited internal memory is inadequate. These delays can be important if the designer wastes significant amounts of time simply waiting for results.

Inevitably some problems are more suited to interactive computing, others to batch processing. In general, where a problem and the solution can be uniquely defined at the outset, batch processing is most suitable, whereas if there is a need to make decisions according to less rigid rules, or simply to express a preference, interactive computing is likely to be more appropriate.

2.4 Computers in design

Whether the computer is being used interactively or in a batch processing mode, we are trying to make use of its ability to process mathematical calculations and logical decisions quickly and accurately. However, as we have seen, the computer is not always as good as the human brain, so we must be careful to identify where in the design process each can be used to greatest advantage. In general, where calculations are carried out according to rigidly defined rules, the computer should be used and where 'judgement' is called for the user should assume control. How this sequence might best be incorporated into the design process will now be discussed.

2.4.1 The design process in civil engineering

Civil engineering design and analysis encompasses an enormous range of problem types. In structural engineering for instance this may include, at one extreme, the determination of loads on a simple structural element and, at the other, the overall design of a major structure such as an offshore oil production platform, or a multi-storey framework. As part of his routine work, the engineer may be concerned with anything between these extremes. However, in all cases there are common stages, each requiring different action, and these may be described diagrammatically as shown in Fig. 2.1.

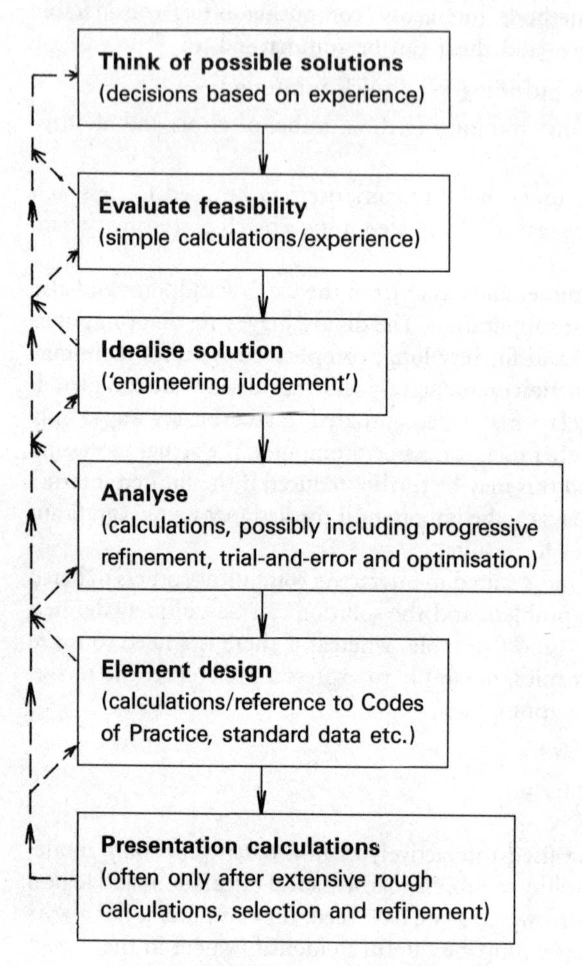

Fig 2.1 Schematic view of the design process in civil engineering

Although this representation implies a linear progression from beginning to end, at almost any stage it may be necessary to go back a number of steps to reconsider isolated aspects or the design as a whole. Thus not only do individual stages involve trial-and-error techniques, but the whole process is largely one of successive refinement.

The relative importance of the various stages depends on the nature and scale of the problem. The design of a simple beam for example involves little 'concept' compared with detail design, whereas a complex three-dimensional structure, such as a multi-storey building, requires much more careful consideration of possible alternative solutions in outline.

Clearly an engineer's activities will typically involve decisions based on judgement, rules or recommendations, calculations, reference to documents such as Codes of Practice, design charts or standard data, and the preparation of presentation calculations. Furthermore, a superficial study of this design process suggests that a considerable amount of his effort is spent on calculations for which the rules are clearly defined (codified rules, standard methods of analysis, etc.), particularly in the latter stages. A closer examination, however, reveals that even in these latter stages the calculations are often punctuated at close intervals with the need for 'engineering judgement' and a typical sequence in a design process may then involve the following steps:

1. Make a guess.
2. Carry out a number of calculations based on that guess according to appropriate rules (e.g. Codes of Practice).
3. On the basis of the results of these calculations, make a decision (e.g. modify original guess or proceed to next stage).

Depending on the decision taken at the third step, the designer may go back to the first step and modify his initial guess, repeating the subsequent operations until he is satisfied, before proceeding to the next sequence. Alternatively, he may find that he needs to modify some earlier decision on the basis of these calculations, and therefore return to the appropriate point in the design process before progressing further.

In the above sequence, the computer can clearly be of potential benefit in the second step, but the designer himself is often better equipped for making guesses and decisions. Whether or not it is worth using a computer for this step depends on how much calculation is required, how difficult and repetitive it is, and what effort is required to define the problem for the computer. The last point is important because, although we may assume that the computer will relieve us of our mundane tasks, the effort of data input can be considerable, and if the advantages to be gained are small, we might be best advised to continue using manual methods.

In some examples the amount of calculation involved in the second step of the design process is considerable, and the benefits of using a computer in such cases are correspondingly great. In other applications it may be easy to formalise the first and third steps and make guesses and decisions automatically to enable several iterations or sequences of operations to be carried out by the computer. In such cases the advantages of using a computer are apparent and there are many examples where computer-aided design has been successfully applied to problems of this type. However, much of the routine work of a designer involves only small amounts of formal calculation before some decision must be made, and in many cases it is difficult or undesirable to allow the program to make such decisions automatically. Work of this nature is not so obviously suited to computer-aided design; indeed, if batch processing were the only form of computing generally available such problems would no doubt continue to be treated by traditional means.

2.4.2 The traditional use of computers in civil engineering

Because interactive computing is a relatively new development, traditional use of computers has been on the basis of batch processing. As a result of the limitations of this mode of operation, the use of computers has been mainly restricted to large, complex problems which could not be reasonably treated by conventional manual methods. An obvious example is the finite element method which has been employed successfully in a wide range of civil engineering design applications. Even here, however, the trial-and-error nature of design has meant that computers have generally been employed only in the later stages of the calculations, often serving as little more than a formal check on less rigorous calculations and a means of producing presentation calculations. This is not to belittle such use, but simply to demonstrate that it has been in terms of very large or complicated projects that computers have traditionally enjoyed greatest application; the more routine work of the designer has been little affected.

One exception to this is the use of automatic design programs, perhaps the most common being the plastic design of steel portal frames. In these the design is 'optimised', generally using a simple criterion of minimum weight, and, having defined the problem, the computer is able to converge on the 'best' solution. Nevertheless, computers have not been implemented on the scale which might have been expected when one considers the amount of time spent on design calculations. This has of course been largely as a result of the unsuitability of batch processing, and the problems associated with slow turnround. However, by using a computer interactively we can now carry out a sequence of calculations, the computer doing the mundane arithmetic and the designer providing the control and making the decisions. As a consequence, a very much wider range of applications becomes suitable for computer-aided design and there seems little doubt that the engineer will be able to take increasing advantage of this valuable design tool in the future.

2.4.3 Effective use of interactive computing

As we have seen, the relatively limited use of computers described above can be attributed to the nature of traditional computing facilities – big, expensive, remote, operating in a batch processing mode, and resulting in a slow turnround. Recent developments now provide almost instant access and immediate turnround together with a fully interactive capability, and this makes it realistic to computerise even relatively simple design tasks. To demonstrate this, consider the example of the design of a simple steel beam. The typical manual procedure followed by an engineer involves various activities and reference to design tables, codified rules and manuals. These are represented diagrammatically in Fig. 2.2.

It is apparent that even for such a simple task the engineer may need, at various stages of the design process, to refer to a number of documents or carry out some simple calculations. By providing the required information within the program and incorporating the necessary calculations, allowing the engineer simply to supply the data, select the trial section sizes and decide – on the basis of the results calculated – whether or not the section is satisfactory, all the tedious work is carried out by the computer. If this represents the rough working to arrive at a suitable solution, presentation calculations can be produced automatically at the end of the run without further interaction from the user.

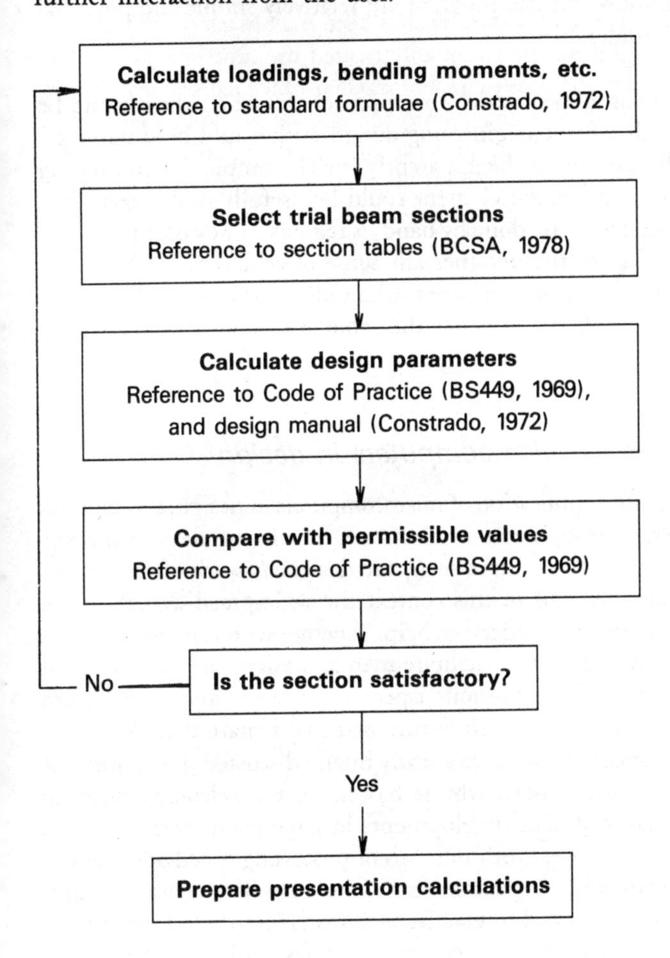

Fig 2.2 The design sequence for a steel beam

It is perhaps worth noting a number of points highlighted by the above example:

(a) The scope of the problem is very limited, the problem itself is relatively simple and well defined, and consequently the program is not a vast complicated piece of software but is simple enough to be written by the engineer himself.

(b) The calculations and procedures adopted are identical to the traditional manual methods. Although these may not always be the most accurate or even efficient in terms of the computer, they do allow the engineer to follow a familiar sequence of design and hence result in a program which is easier to use.
(c) The computer does none of the engineering: it is acting simply as a reference manual and calculator – not a decision maker.
(d) Although the application and the program are relatively simple the potential benefits are not inconsiderable.

There are many other similar tasks to which the approach described above could be applied. Indeed, almost all routine engineering design work would be suitable for this type of simple application. Even the apparently trivial example of determining loads on a structure or on a particular element could be usefully undertaken on a computer used in this way. This task, done by hand, is tedious, time-consuming and is certainly not one which gives the designer any sense of achievement. With the increasing use of limit state design and the need to consider a range of loading cases, the calculation effort is multiplied and hence the value of computer application is increased.

2.5 The particular role of microcomputers in design

In trying to assess the potential application of microcomputers in design, it is perhaps worth reflecting on recent developments in electronic calculating devices and the consequences for the designer. As we have seen, the designer's work often involves lengthy numerical calculations, and in this context the widespread availability of electronic calculators has been of considerable help. Together with numerous design charts and tables which have evolved to facilitate manual design, the calculator has relieved the engineer of some of the laborious aspects of his work, and there cannot be many who would welcome back the slide rule and mathematical tables.

At the other end of the spectrum we have already briefly discussed the mainframe computer and suggested some reasons why it has not been welcomed quite as unreservedly as the calculator. Recent developments in large computers have seen a continuing increase in their power, both in terms of processing speed and the size of problems which can be treated. At the same time, there has been a move towards greater ease of use with terminals and interactive facilities. Nevertheless, the cost of use and the lack of suitable software on larger computers has resulted in their rather limited use by designers, particularly for routine applications. The micro falls naturally between the calculator and the bigger computer and we feel it is important to decide whether as such it is a very powerful calculator, a very small, cheap version of traditional computers, or something quite different.

In principle the micro can be used in the same way as either a traditional computer or a calculator. Used without a program it can operate as a calculator – albeit a rather expensive one – and it could equally well operate in a batch processing mode. However, it should be clear that neither mode of operation takes full advantage of both its substantial computing power and its immediate accessibility. In terms of its cost, accessibility and mode of use, the microcomputer is much more an extension of the programmable calculator, but in power and speed it has more in common with the traditional computer. With reference to convenience and ease of use it is superior to both.

It would appear therefore that anything which is currently done using an electronic calculator (programmable or non-programmable) could be done using a microcomputer, and that some of the work currently processed on a large mainframe or minicomputer may be capable of being processed on a micro. Whether a particular problem is suitable for solution using a microcomputer will depend on a number of factors, an important one being the availability of good quality software (this point will be discussed more fully in Chapter 6), but it would seem that the micro is going to affect the routine work of the designer in a much greater way than the electronic calculator has done. Its obvious attraction is in terms of cost, for, although many mainframe computer installations now provide an interactive computing facility, the cost of using this for routine work may be prohibitive. In contrast, the microcomputer provides a facility which is, by its very nature, a 'dedicated' machine ideal for interactive use. Both capital costs and recurrent costs are low, and many firms have found that a single job has enabled them to recoup their modest investment.

However, microcomputers do not provide an ideal solution to all problems. Large 'number crunching' analyses are more appropriately tackled on bigger computers and, although it is not surprising that plane frame analysis figured prominently among the first programs which were commercially available on micros, there are many applications which are much more suited to the particular features of these small systems. Microcomputers should therefore be seen alongside larger computers as one of the tools which has a place in design offices, each of which will have its own specific computing requirements. Whilst very small firms may be reliant on a microcomputer to process a wide range of problems, some larger organisations are recognising that there is an appropriate role for micros as well as minis, mainframes and bureau services. A well-planned microcomputer installation in a design office can therefore make a valuable contribution to the efficiency of that office, and can do so in a very positive way at modest cost.

Whilst many of the applications for which a microcomputer may be suitable can – and indeed currently are – treated manually, significant savings in a designer's time can be realised. Furthermore, these savings are often associated with tedious calculations, allowing the designer to devote more of his attention to the 'engineering'. The fact that a computer is not necessary for many applications should not tempt us to adopt a scornful attitude towards its use. The great majority of commercial type applications – payroll, accounts, etc. – involve almost trivial calculations, but this has not prevented the successful exploitation of computers by the business world. Engineers too should welcome the introduction of micros as design aids and see them as a development similar to design charts and tables which have evolved to assist manual design methods. The potential benefits of microcomputers are, however, likely to be much greater than these more traditional aids.

Having discussed the potential for computer-aided design in civil engineering with particular reference to microcomputers, we now need to look in greater detail at how best to introduce micros into the design office. In the next chapters we shall present a description of the physical components of a microcomputer system, and then proceed to consider how they can be used to greatest effect.

Chapter 3

The components of a microcomputer system

In this chapter we shall consider some of the technical intricacies of microcomputers. We make no apology for involving the reader in the complexities of the structure of a microcomputer and its associated equipment because there are many aspects which potential users must be aware of in their selection of a system. The microcomputer market is extremely competitive and, without some background knowledge, a buyer can be overawed by technical specifications and misguided by smooth-talking computer salesmen. We shall explain the principles of how microcomputers work and how these fundamentals dictate the characteristics and limitations of different systems.

3.1 Bits, Bytes and Bus

Every engineer knows that computers work to the binary system of numbers 0–1. The binary system can represent any two mutually exclusive states: on/off, yes/no; or in the case of electronics: voltage existing/voltage not existing. Any number may be represented in the binary system by a series of zeros and ones, as shown in Table 3.1.

Table 3.1 Binary representation of decimal numbers

Binary number	Decimal equivalent
1	1
10	2
11	3
100	4
1101011	107
101011100110	2 790

Each 0 or 1 is the smallest piece of information that can be represented in a computer and each is known as a 'bit' – a contraction of '***bi**nary dig**it***'. The main feature of cheaper microcomputers is that the microprocessor combines 8 bits together to produce a 'byte' and most operations are carried out by transferring and transforming bytes. An 8-bit byte can take any state between 00000000 and 1111111 – i.e. 256 different states; therefore 1 byte can easily represent the numbers 0–9, upper and lower case alphabetic characters, over 30 standard printable non-alphabetic characters, as well as many control characters required in computer operation.

A byte is transferred around a microcomputer on a 'data bus' consisting, in effect, of eight parallel wires which call at all relevant points and which form a data highway. A single byte can represent a unique instruction or several bytes can be combined together to represent numbers and transmitted together along the data bus.

The computer memory is organised into a large number of memory 'registers' which can be considered as a two-dimensional matrix of pigeon-holes. Each register is capable of storing 1 byte (8 bits) of information. Each memory register can be 'addressed' by specifying the location of the register. Whereas 1 byte can only be used to specify a register location in the range 0–255, 2 bytes are actually combined to achieve a 256 × 256 or 65 536 addressing capability. A microcomputer therefore requires an 'address bus' consisting of 16 parallel wires to be able to transmit the address of a register. An 8-bit microcomputer with a 2-byte (16-bit) address bus will therefore have a maximum of 65 536 possible memory registers which will probably include all memory required for system operation, programming language, user's program, etc. Such a microcomputer will be referred to as having a '64K byte' addressing capability where 1K (kilo) byte is 1 024 or 2^{10} bytes. Although 8-bit micros can address 64K of memory, the actual memory available in a system depends on how many memory chips have actually been installed. It may be possible for a 8K, 8-bit micro to be incremented in size to 64K by literally inserting additional memory chips.

Since 1982 we have witnessed the greater availability of 16-bit microcomputers. From the preceding argument it is evident that a 16-bit byte and a 2-byte (32-bit) address bus could have an addressing capability of 65 536 squared. While 16-bit micros are now becoming more widely available, we shall limit our discussion in this chapter to 8-bit microcomputers; exactly the same principles of computer operation apply to 8-bit and 16-bit microprocessors. The normal practical limitation to the memory size therefore depends on the number of bits in a byte and how many bytes are in the address bus.

An example of the practical significance of 1K byte (1 024 bytes) is that 1 byte can represent any alphabetic character, so 1 024 characters of text can be stored in 1K of memory – about half a page of text in this book. Generally, integer numbers require 2 bytes, allowing 500 to be stored, while real numbers require 4 bytes, allowing 250 numbers to be stored in one K.

3.2 Memory types

There are two types of internal memory of relevance to micro users – Read Only Memory (ROM) and Random Access Memory (RAM). ROM is permanent memory (it cannot be changed) used to store system instructions and sometimes language interpreters required to operate the computer, and is usually unique to any one make of microcomputer. The manufacturer has implanted certain instructions and logic into ROM which can be 'read' (i.e. the contents of the register can be transferred to another register) but which cannot be changed by the user. When the computer is switched on ROM is immediately active and accessible; on switching off, information in ROM is not available, but it is not lost.

RAM (Random Access Memory) is a slight misnomer, a better description would be 'Read/Write' Memory. RAM is the memory available for the user to store program instructions or data, or for storing instructions to operate and control peripheral equipment (particularly mass storage systems). The contents of any one memory register may vary between successive uses of the computer and information in RAM is lost forever when the computer is switched off. RAM is therefore referred to as being 'volatile'. From the user's point of view, the amount of available RAM is important because the total amount of ROM and RAM cannot exceed the installed memory capacity or the computer's addressing capability. Obviously if a considerable amount of memory is reserved by ROM, the amount of 'user-RAM' will be limited for storing the user's programs or data. Unfortunately different micro manufacturers quote RAM in a variety of ways and it is not always exactly clear what is available for the user.

There are several other memory types which are of little relevance to our applications. It is possible to buy 'Programmable Read Only Memory' (PROM) which can be permanently programmed using special microprocessor equipment, or 'Erasable Programmable Read Only Memory' (EPROM) which can be both programmed and erased. Both memory types allow ROM programs to be available as soon as the computer is switched on.

3.3 The central processor unit

The heart of a microcomputer is the microprocessor containing a Central Processor Unit (CPU). The CPU organises the way in which operations are carried out and controls the use of ROM, RAM, data and address bus, and communication with the outside world as shown in Fig. 3.1.

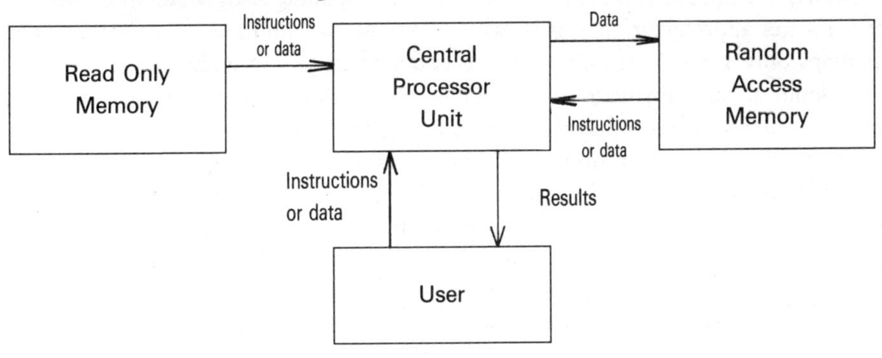

Fig. 3.1

On commands given by the user the CPU carries out a series of instructions as defined by the contents of ROM or RAM registers. As an example, when the micro is switched on the CPU automatically refers to a part of ROM to execute what is often referred to as the 'monitor' program. This is specific to a particular make of micro and is the lowest form of communication between the user and the computer. Some monitor programs may allow the user to inspect a ROM register, to inspect or change the contents of a RAM register or to run a 'machine language' program by using monitor command codes. Other monitor programs may display a simple message or instruction for the user to insert a disc.

The instructions followed by the CPU are 8-bit codes stored in successive memory registers. The first instruction will be fetched from the first memory location and copied into a CPU 'register' where it will be translated and the appropriate action carried out. The CPU will then fetch the next instruction, execute it, and so on. This sequence of operations is known as the 'fetch-execute' cycle. The instruction codes are known as the 'instruction set' or 'machine code' and are unique to the particular microprocessor used in the microcomputer. The codes refer to relatively simple operations which are carried out at extremely high speed. For example, in micros using the 6502 microprocessor the process of adding two stored numbers together and placing the result into another memory store requires three operations – transferring the first number to the CPU, adding the second number to the first and transferring the result to memory. Each of these operations would require at least three fetches or executes – say about ten cycles for the one addition. The total computing time therefore depends on how quickly the microprocessor can execute a cycle.

The speed of execution of the fetch-execute cycles depends on the 'clock speed'; every microprocessor has a built in 'clock' which will carry out one operation (a fetch, execute, etc.) at regular intervals of time. Microprocessors typically have clock speeds of between 1 and 8 MHz, allowing 1–8 million operations/second. In the above example of addition using a 6502 with a 1 MHz clock speed, about 100 000 such ten-cycle additions can be carried out in one second. This immediately demonstrates the power of the microprocessors to carry out relatively simple tasks at very high speed. However, some apparently simple commands like obtaining a trigonometrical function use a series approximation which may require many hundreds of clock cycles and perhaps only 1 000 functions could be obtained in one second.

A series of such instructions could be entered into memory by specifying binary codes for each operation, but the process would be extremely complex and arduous. This method of programming is known as 'machine-code programming' and the user requires a very detailed knowledge of the internal workings of the specific CPU being used. This approach is obviously totally unrealistic for our purposes, but a description of the method has been presented because, although in practice we use a higher level of programming language, any language will eventually convert instructions into exactly the same form of machine code as described above.

There are very much easier ways of transferring instructions to memory based on different language levels. One of these languages (assembly language) will be discussed in this chapter because it still requires a good knowledge of the workings of the microcomputer. Other higher-level languages which are virtually independent of the make of microcomputer will be discussed in Chapters 4 and 5.

3.4 Assembly language

To ease the burden of machine language programming an 'assembly' language can be used. Again, this is specific to the type of microprocessor, but it uses mnemonics to represent machine codes. The programmer has a set of 50 to 60 mnemonics in the assembly language which are converted by an 'assembly/assembler' program into the appropriate 8-bit binary machine codes. The programmer still needs to know the detailed internal workings of the CPU, but it is a definite improvement on machine-code programming. The assembler is sometimes available in ROM, but more usually it has to be loaded into RAM prior to using the assembly language. Although it is unlikely that we would ever want to learn the intricacies of a CPU in order to use assembly language, there are several obvious applications in which there may be distinct advantages – largely concerned with computing speed. The main benefit of a set of machine-code instructions is that they can be executed at extremely high speed because instructions do not have to be converted from a higher level of programming language. We shall see in Chapter 4 that the use of other higher-level languages can be quite slow and may not be appropriate, for example, if we need to process a large amount of data very quickly. The use of a microcomputer to collect data from measuring instruments (strain gauges, etc.) is a very cheap and efficient way of recording data for instantaneous analysis, but the rate of input of data may be too fast unless a machine-code program produced by an assembler program is used. Similarly, complex iterative procedures in finite element analysis could be accelerated by the use of a normal high-level language program which includes a machine-code data processing routine.

We have presented the basic workings of the microprocessor and how microprocessor instructions and data can be stored in memory and addressed. The microprocessor and memory can be combined with additional equipment to allow the user to communicate with the microprocessor, and to allow the permanent storage of programs and data to produce a complete microcomputer system. The following sections will present a description of the input and output devices and the different methods of mass storage.

3.5 Communicating with the computer

Figure 3.2 shows the lines of communication required between the user, the computer and the mass storage.

Communication between the user and the CPU is normally achieved by the use of a keyboard and a VDU, although a keyboard and a printer are equally effective but considerably slower.

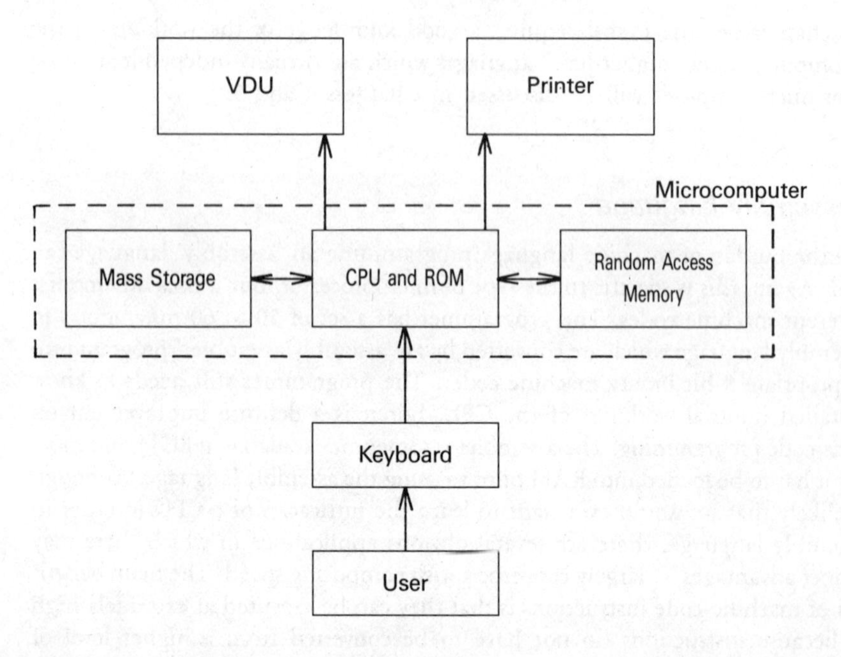

Fig 3.2 Communicating with a microcomputer

3.5.1 Keyboard

The normal way of transferring information (instructions, data, a program, etc.) from the user to the computer is by the use of a typewriter-like keyboard as shown in Fig. 3.3. When a character key is depressed a series of bits representing the binary code for the key is transferred to the CPU where it is automatically interpreted and the appropriate character displayed on the VDU or printer. The binary codes used for the characters are known as the 'ASCII' codes (American Standard Code for Information Interchange) and have become the standard method for encoding all alphanumeric characters, symbols and control codes. The ASCII code is in fact used at every point in the microcomputer; if the letter 'A' is stored in a memory register, the 8-bits of the byte will be the ASCII coding for 'A'.

The main difference between the layout of a microcomputer keyboard and a conventional typewriter keyboard is that there are at least three additional keys – RESET, CTRL (Control) and RETURN keys.

If the RESET key is pressed the computer will automatically return to the monitor program, losing any high-level language program or data that was being used (i.e. the contents of RAM cannot be recovered). In some systems this is the only way of getting out of a program which has 'hung-up' (usually the program has locked into an infinite processing loop) because of a programming fault.

The CTRL key is a special function key which, when pressed at the same time as another key, will carry out an alternative instruction. Some micros use the CTRL and another character to allow a program to be stopped during execution, while others use it to cancel previous instructions or to control the way in which output is presented on the VDU.

Fig. 3.3 The DEC Rainbow keyboard

The RETURN key is the key that must be pressed when the user wants to return control to the computer. When the computer is asking for information from the user the data must first be typed onto the keyboard, then the RETURN key pressed for the computer to accept the data and to continue execution.

Many lower-cost micros will have additional non-standard characters on the keyboard, particularly for the use of low resolution graphics. The Commodore series has a range of graphics characters, as does the Sinclair Spectrum as shown in Fig. 3.4.

The quality of the keyboard is extremely important. While the reliability of the microprocessor itself can be very good because all the components are based on electronic circuitry, the keyboard is an electro-mechanical device in which the physical movement of the key causes two contacts to close together. While only requiring fairly light pressure to depress a key, the keyboard has to tolerate annoyance or frustration expressed by a user's brute force. Some of the early micros had relatively cheap keyboards which resulted in the complete failure of the contacts or produced the multiple transmission of a character from only one key depression (known as 'keybounce'). Such problems have now been largely overcome by the use of more resilient professional keyboards, but for anybody who has become accustomed to using brute force on the old mechanical typewriters, we would strongly recommend (through bitter experience) that they should take some instruction on 'touch-typing'.

Fig. 3.4 A Commodore keyboard, showing an alternative character set on each key

3.5.2 Visual display unit

The VDU is the more usual form of communication from the micro to the user. Although a VDU is not essential, it provides a very fast and neat way of presenting information. The main limitation is that the VDU information is not permanent because it can be over-written by subsequent information. However, we shall be arguing in Chapter 6 that when running an application program, the output to the VDU is the equivalent of a rough working sheet which would probably be discarded on reaching a final design.

The information presented on a VDU results from previous instructions from a user or preprogrammed message or displays from the computer, as shown in Fig. 3.5. We have already seen that when a keyboard character key is pressed, it is automatically displayed on the VDU so the user can see what information has been entered. The visual displays used on most micros tend to be referred to as 'memory-mapped' displays because the information on the VDU is a 'map' of one section of the micro's RAM. We shall see in Chapter 4 that one section of RAM is reserved for the screen display and the VDU can be thought of as a 'window' showing the contents of that part of RAM. The CPU constantly scans the VDU section of RAM and translates the binary contents of each memory register from its ASCII equivalent which is displayed at the appropriate position on the VDU. If any memory register in the VDU RAM is changed, then the screen display is changed.

Many micros are supplied with an integral purpose-built VDU as shown in Fig. 3.6, while others can accommodate any normal domestic television without modification. An old television is certainly a cheap way of providing a VDU, but a certain amount of screen flickering and mains interference can cause eye strain if it is used for long sessions. Alternatively a proper monitor can be used which provides screen stability and good picture resolution, but at a higher cost.

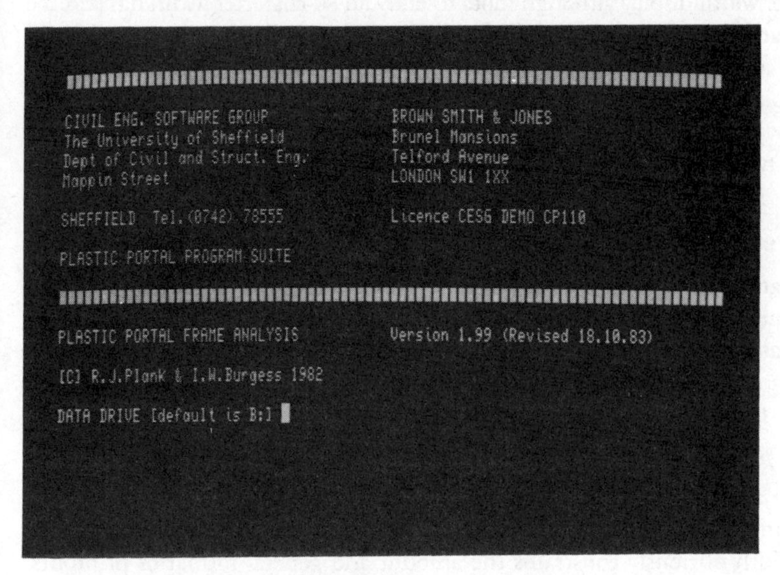

Fig. 3.5 A typical display on a VDU

Fig. 3.6 Intertec Superbrain with an integral VDU

The number of characters displayed on the VDU depends on the make of microcomputer, not the physical size of the VDU. Many microcomputers started with a 40-character width display although more recently an 80-character width has become more popular. The number of lines on the VDU can vary between micros, but 24 seems to be an accepted standard. For a micro with a 40 × 24 character memory-mapped display, 960 memory registers (960 bytes, or nearly 1K), are required in RAM to provide the display. These memory registers are contained within the 64K maximum addressable memory of an 8-bit microcomputer.

3.5.3 Printers

A printer is an essential output device in computer-aided design because of the need for a permanent record of the data used in the design and of the results produced by the program. The variety of the printers is as great as the variety of microcomputers, although the price plays a much bigger part in printers.

There are three basic types of printers.

1. *Tally roll printers.*

   These use a narrow roll (2 to 3 inches wide) of paper which is often charge- or heat-sensitive. While the printer may be cheap, the special paper can be expensive and its width obviously constrains the amount and general format of printouts.

2. *Dot matrix printers.*

   These are the most common type of printer used for printing the results of computer-aided design and a typical dot matrix printer is shown in Fig. 3.7. The printed characters are produced by a 9 × 5 or 7 × 5 matrix of dots as shown in Fig. 3.8. Most dot matrix printers can print 80 characters across the page at 10 characters per inch and can compress the character size to about 16 to 17 characters per inch (about 132 characters across the page). Printing speeds vary from between 30 and 240 characters per second, but while the quality of the print is adequate for a permanent copy of a design or for draft reports, and can be photo-copied, it is not good enough for final reports or letters.

3. *Typewriter quality printers.*

   For high quality printout a 'daisywheel' type of printer is essential. These can use standard typewriter daisywheels and either fabric or carbon ribbons to produce the same print quality as an electric typewriter, but printing speeds can be slow (between about 15 and 60 characters per second, depending very much on prices, which range between £400 and £2 000). A useful alternative is to purchase a standard electronic typewriter which has a communications interface so that it can be used as a printer. The Olivetti ET121 and Olympia Scripta typewriters can be supplied with a standard interface at relatively small additional cost.

The main benefit of more expensive printers lies in reliability. A printer is a much more mechanical device than any other computer peripheral and a cheaper (and therefore mechanically inferior) printer may create more problems of reliability than the saving in price can offer.

One of the most difficult aspects of attaching a printer to a micro is what is known as 'interfacing'. The micro and printer will probably be made by two completely

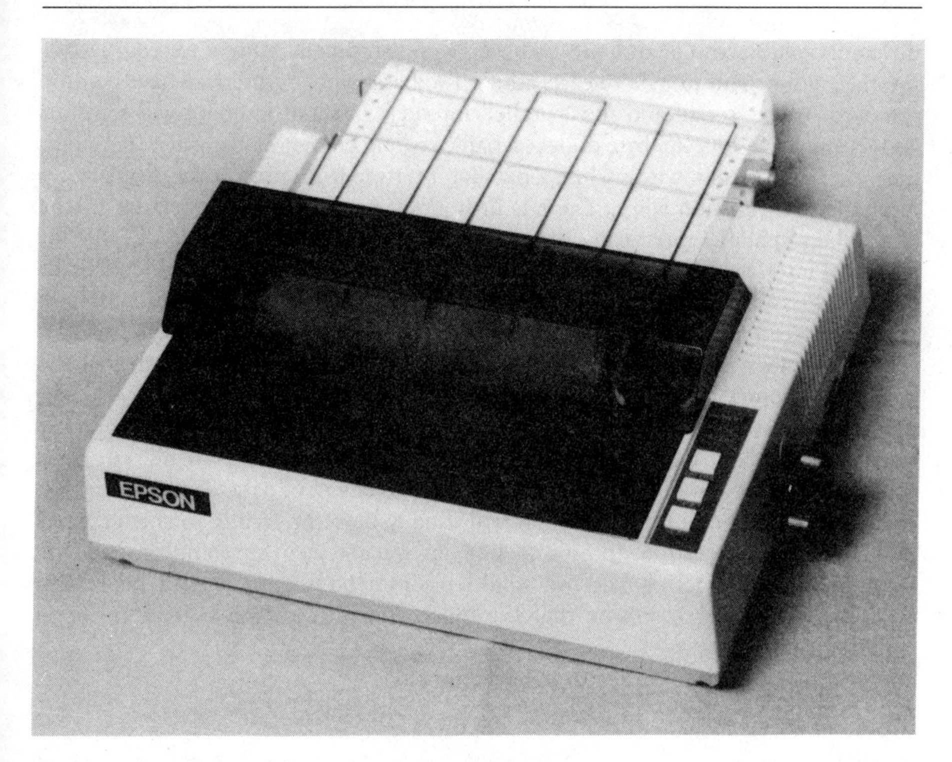

Fig. 3.7 A typical 80 column dot matrix printer

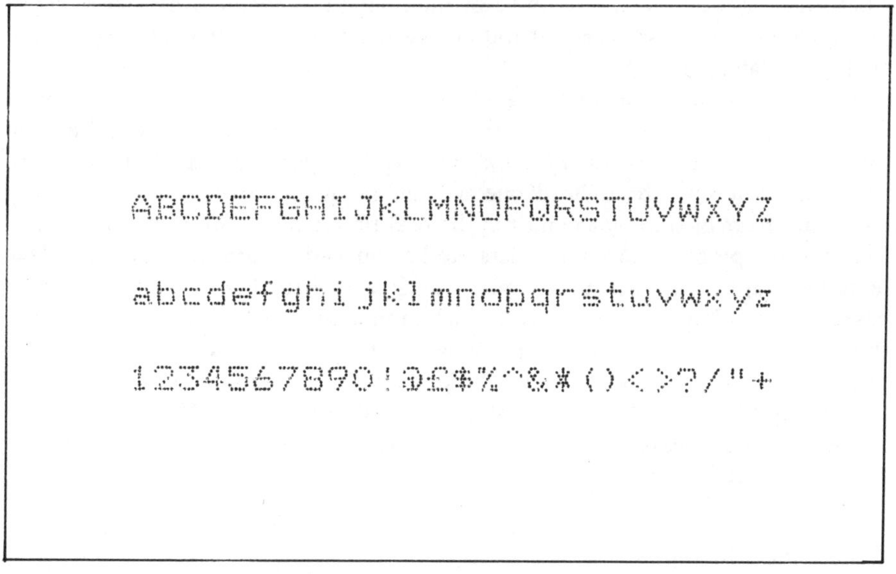

ABCDEFGHIJKLMNOPQRSTUVWXYZ

abcdefghijklmnopqrstuvwxyz

1234567890!@£$%^&*()<>?/"+

Fig. 3.8 Dot matrix printout showing how individual characters are constructed from a series of dots

different manufacturers and the two pieces of equipment must have compatible interfacing for them to 'talk to each other'. Two basic types of interface have become standard – the 'serial' and the 'parallel' interface. A serial interface will transmit and receive the 8-bits of a byte of data serially, i.e. one bit behind the other (requiring only one transmission wire), while a parallel interface will transmit the 8 bits along 8 parallel transmission wires. There is little point in discussing the relative merits of serial and parallel interfacing methods except to say that the length of cable for a parallel interface is limited to only a few feet in length. The main problem is that both micro and printer must have the same type of interface. Micros usually have both interface types either as a standard or an optional fitting. The most common specification for a serial interface is the 'RS232C' and the most common for the parallel is the 'Centronics' type.

However, the problem does not end here because both computer and printer must transmit and receive data at the same transmission rates (known as 'baud' rate) and with some 'protocol' of data conversion, acknowledgement of data, data transmission check etc. Both computer and printer will usually have the facility to change baud rate and communications protocol, but interfacing can be complex and the terminology intimidating and we would recommend that it should be left to equipment suppliers to ensure that the micro and printer have both been set to communicate properly.

3.5.4 Mass storage

Some form of mass storage is essential for computer-aided design for two reasons. First, the amount of user RAM in the micro is finite and may not be sufficient for a particular application; and second, any information (program or data) in RAM is lost when the micro is switched off and we may need to retain copies of the program or data for later use.

If insufficient internal memory is available for an application, a mass storage device can also give an almost infinite increase in memory accessible by the CPU. Although this is less likely to be necessary in analysis or design programs compared with business management, it is possible to 'load' one program into RAM, run it, 'save' the resulting data onto the mass store, load and run the next program by reading the saved data from the last program, save more data, and so on as discussed in section 8.7. The more likely applications requiring mass storage are where a fairly simple program has to analyse a large amount of data which cannot all be held in RAM at the same time. In this case the program would remain in RAM and would read in successive blocks of data from the mass store. The problem of accessing mass storage is that it is very much slower than if the information all existed in RAM.

There are two types of mass storage of relevance to computer-aided design, namely cassette tape and floppy disc.

3.5.5 Cassette tapes

Cassette tape storage can vary between the cheap domestic audio tapes to higher speed purpose-designed tapes supplied with a few of the more expensive computer systems. Although most cheaper micros can use cassette tape, many of the more professional systems cannot. As floppy-disc systems become cheaper, there will be a gradual move away from cassette storage.

Information is stored on the magnetic surface of the cheaper tapes as a series of binary digits which have been converted into audible tones – one for the digit 0, another tone for the digit 1. The way in which this is done, and the exact format of the information, varies considerably between different micros, to such an extent that it is virtually impossible to save information from one micro on a tape and to use the tape to load the same information into a different make of micro.

Several micros are supplied with an integral cassette deck as shown in Fig. 3.9, while many others allow the use of almost any domestic cassette recorder with a microphone input socket and auxilliary output socket. This allows a very cheap method of mass storage, but there are many disadvantages in cassette systems.

Fig. 3.9 A Sharp microcomputer with an integral cassette recorder

One of the main problems again concerns reliability; because of the conversion from digital to audio signals it is not uncommon for data to be recorded incorrectly because of poorly aligned or dirty recording heads and because of variations of motor speed in the cassette recorder. If data has been incorrectly saved and the computer has been switched off, the information can be lost completely. While this problem can be alleviated to a certain extent by making several separate recordings of the information and by using a facility available on some micros to verify that the saved information is correct, the frustration and the cost of losing data can be considerable.

If a cassette store system works well (and many systems do) the other main problem is the way in which the data is stored and the speed of retrieval. Data is stored on tape in a 'serial' format; the first item of data is stored first, the second item is stored next, and so on. If one particular item needs to be retrieved from the mass store and it happens to occur half way through the tape, all of the preceding data must be accessed first before the required item can be retrieved. In other words, information cannot be retrieved selectively. This makes the use of a tape system for mass data (as opposed to program) storage a slow process. However, a tape system should not be undervalued if relatively unsophisticated 'utility' programs are used requiring no access to data in mass storage. Such programs can be stored on individual tapes and loaded as required using data provided by the user through the keyboard. The time to load the program is certainly much greater than using a floppy disc, but the difference in cost between the two systems may justify the waste of a few minutes to load a tape program.

The amount of information that can be saved on a cassette is simply a function of the length of the tape. One common recording standard can save about 2K of data/minute, so a 30-minute cassette tape is capable of storing 60K of continuous information but it would take 30 minutes to transfer to and from the computer. By using a large number of tapes, the capacity of mass storage is almost limitless.

A few of the more expensive micro systems provide more expensive but more reliable tape systems. These tend to be high quality digital (not audio) recorders with properly controlled motor speed and the facility to carry out a fast search on a tape to find the beginning of the data required.

3.5.6 Floppy discs

A floppy disc is exactly what its name suggests: it is a thin flexible plastic disc coated with a tough metallic oxide and contains recorded information on either one or both sides. Two standard sizes are available – $5\frac{1}{4}$ inch and 8 inch diameter. The disc is contained permanently in a thin protective cardboard jacket as shown in Fig. 3.10 and has cut-out holes to allow a recording head to access each part of the disc. The disc and its protective cover are inserted into a disc drive as shown in Fig. 3.11 containing a spindle which rotates the disc at between 300 and 360 rpm. A recording head moves over the surface of the disc and is able to transfer information to and from any specified part of the disc.

There are many benefits of a disc mass store system. There is no doubt that a disc system is very much more reliable than cassette tape, but its main benefit lies in the speed of accessing and transferring data, and the fact that information can be retrieved selectively.

Information is stored on floppy discs in addressable 'tracks' and 'sectors'. Fig. 3.12 shows a disc having 35 concentric tracks, each track containing 16 sectors, as used in the Apple II DOS 3.2 system with a $5\frac{1}{4}$ inch disc drive. Four tracks are reserved for information to control and organise the disc system while the remaining 31 tracks are available for the user to store information. Each of the 31 tracks has 16 sectors each capable of storing 256 bytes (0.25K). The maximum user storage capacity

Fig. 3.10 A $5\frac{1}{4}$ inch floppy disc

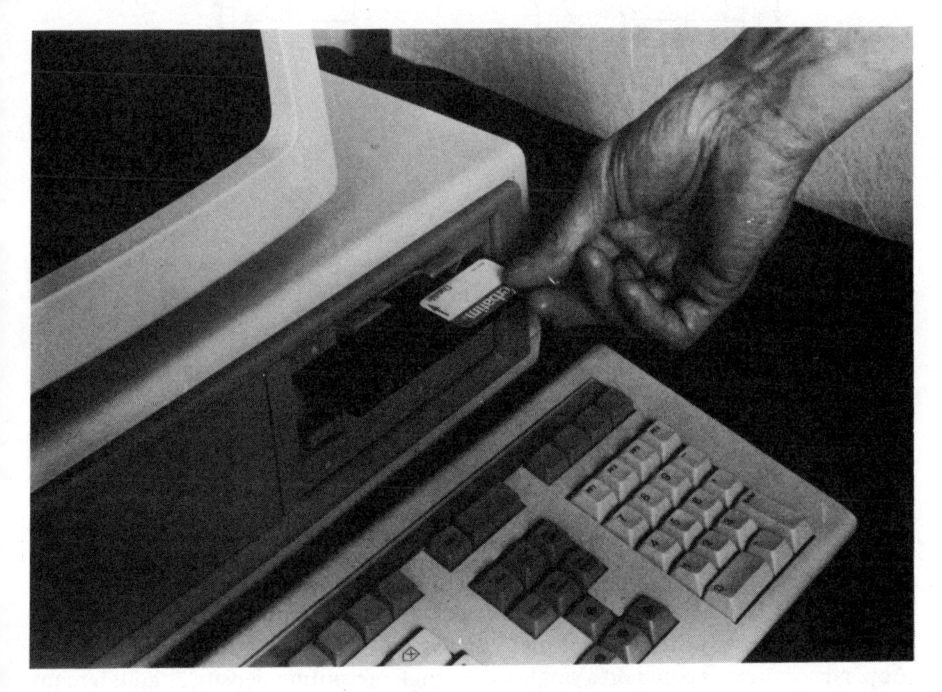

Fig. 3.11 Inserting a floppy disc into a DEC Rainbow

is therefore about 125K. From the user's point of view, access to any particular track and sector is almost immediate, taking less than a second to start the disc drive and to transfer 1K of data.

In practice, the user needs to know nothing about what is contained in the tracks and sectors, because a simple set of commands is available in the 'Operating System' to be described in Chapter 4. If a program is to be transferred from the micro's RAM onto the disc, the user need only specify the word 'SAVE' with a unique reference name (a 'filename') for the program to be transferred automatically to the disc. If the user wants to recall the program at a later date he can ask for the program of the specified filename to be loaded, and the Operating System and disc drive will do the work.

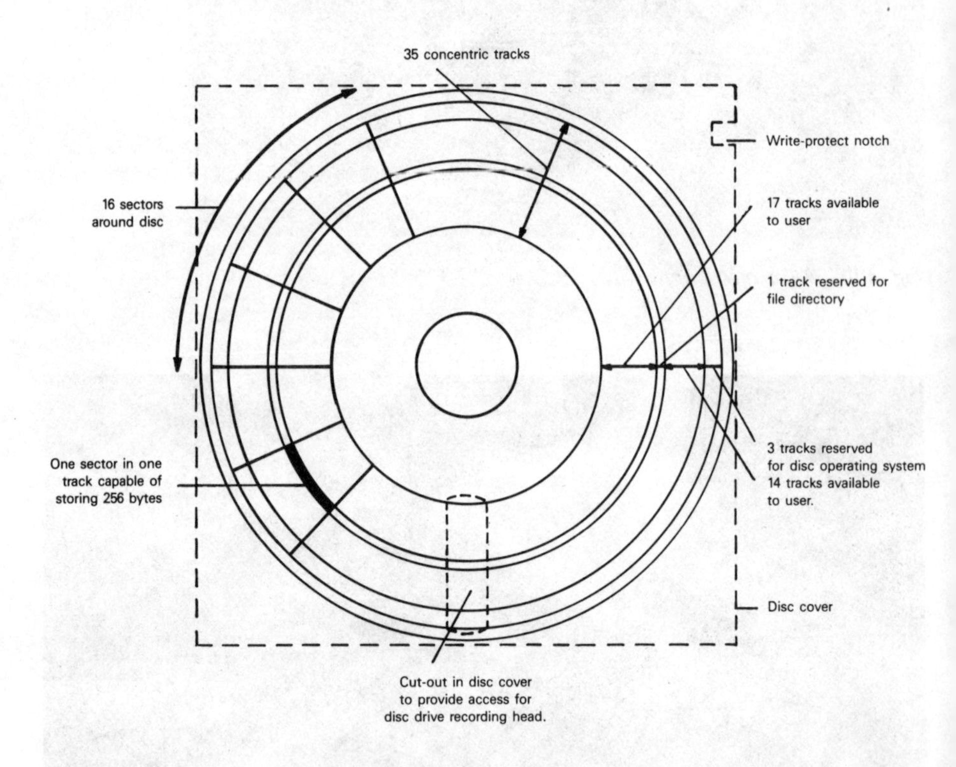

Fig. 3.12 Layout of tracks and sectors on an Apple II disc

The benefits of a disc mass store are therefore considerable, but even a single $5\frac{1}{4}$ inch disc drive can be about ten times more expensive than a cassette recorder. There also exists a wide range of disc systems with a variety of capacities. A single Apple disc system is based on a single side, 'single' recording density although many other systems have double sided and double or quadruple density recording – giving over one megabyte of storage on a $5\frac{1}{4}$ inch disc. An 8 inch disc system can store proportionally more, again depending on whether it is single or double sided and the recording density. Obviously, the correct type of disc (in terms of the number of recording sides and data density) needs to be purchased for the micro to be used.

Smaller 'microdrives' have recently been introduced for the cheaper home computers. For example, the Sinclair Spectrum now has an 85K disc drive using special cartridges at a fraction of the price of a $5\frac{1}{4}$ inch disc system. While such innovation and price reduction is welcome, there is the danger that different computer manufacturers will produce their own disc systems which are unable to accommodate discs from other manufacturers' computers. The general observation is that the larger the disc, the more likely it is that it may be used on a different make of computer. The 8 inch disc systems, for example, are derived from mainframe and minicomputer systems using a common data format. Although there is only a relatively small number of different $5\frac{1}{4}$ inch systems manufactured, they are used in varying ways by the hundreds of makes of computers sold. While it is still difficult to take a $5\frac{1}{4}$ inch disc from one make of computer and use it on another, the use of a standard size is at least the first step towards a complete standardisation of data formats.

The reliability of floppy disc systems is surprisingly good, bearing in mind the high speed of rotation of the disc and the very fine degree of engineering required to allow the recording head to be positioned in exactly the right place on the disc. The recording head in fact touches the disc when reading or writing information, but very little wear of the disc occurs. Disc lives of the order of one million passes of the recording head over the disc surface, and a recording head life of 20 000 hours of contact with floppy discs need hardly be of concern in view of the limited amount of use for our applications.

The benefits of a floppy disc mass store become even more apparent in applications requiring a large amount of data manipulation involving the transfer of data from one disc to another. Most micros will support two disc drives, others will operate many more drives, each of which can be accessed selectively from within an application program. For most computer-aided analysis and design applications (to be discussed later in this book) a single disc drive is often adequate. However, two disc drives allow a program disc to be used in one drive and a data disc in the other drive, and also enables easier production of back-up copies of programs or data.

3.5.7 Other mass storage systems

For even larger mass storage a much more expensive 'hard disc' (sometimes known as 'Winchester') can be used with micros. This consists of a stack of rigid discs which is either permanently fixed or removable and all of which can be accessed at the same time. Storage capacities of 5 – 300 megabytes are available but relatively expensive. Some micros, for example the ACT Sirius and Apricot, can use a small 5 megabyte hard disc in place of one of the floppy discs, while a larger hard disc system may be attached as a separate unit. The current rate of innovation will obviously result in even greater capacity floppy and hard disc systems. A recent alternative to a disc system is 'disc-cache' – an additional random access memory bank which will receive or send data to the computer's memory. This would be used instead of, but in the same way as, a disc for applications using large amounts of data which cannot be stored in the computer's memory. While the main benefit is considerably improved processing time, disc-cache is volatile and its contents must eventually be transferred to disc for permanent storage.

3.6 Computer graphics

For many years mainframe and minicomputers have provided graphics facilities for engineering design. There exist many impressive systems on larger computers to enter and display information graphically and to produce scaled drawings. While the cost of graphics facilities may not be justified for the type of applications discussed in this book, it is worth considering the extent of graphics facilities available on micros and the range of peripheral graphics equipment.

3.6.1 Computer-displayed graphics

In this section we shall concentrate on the hardware requirements for graphics while in Chapter 4 we shall consider the question of graphics software.

As explained in section 3.5.2, the VDU display is a 'map' of one section of the micro's RAM. When a key on the keyboard is depressed, the 'value' of the key is automatically transferred to part of RAM which is being constantly inspected by the VDU. (The VDU can be thought of as a window showing the contents of the memory.) Similarly when a program is running and results have to be presented on the VDU, the results are, in fact, transferred to the part of RAM which is being scanned and the memory contents are displayed on the VDU. This is known as a 'memory-mapped' screen display. Any text characters can therefore only be displayed on the screen if they exist in the part of RAM mapped by the VDU.

All micros will have the ability to produce 'low-resolution' graphics using the principles of the memory map. The building blocks of the low resolution graphics would be any of the normally available keyboard characters, although several cheaper micros have many additional characters for this purpose, each based on a constant character size, but with different shapes depicted within the block. Fig. 3.13 shows the sort of display that can be built up using the character set available on the keyboard. The use of low resolution graphics is obviously limited and may only be appropriate in a program to 'draw' shapes to convey information or instructions to the user. A more useful application could be the construction of histograms based on survey data.

High resolution graphics facilities vary from micro to micro according to both the hardware and software available. Some micros, have 'built-in' graphics – part of the 64K of memory can be reserved for graphics data, but high resolution graphics, as the name implies, uses a much smaller element (known as a 'pixel') as its building

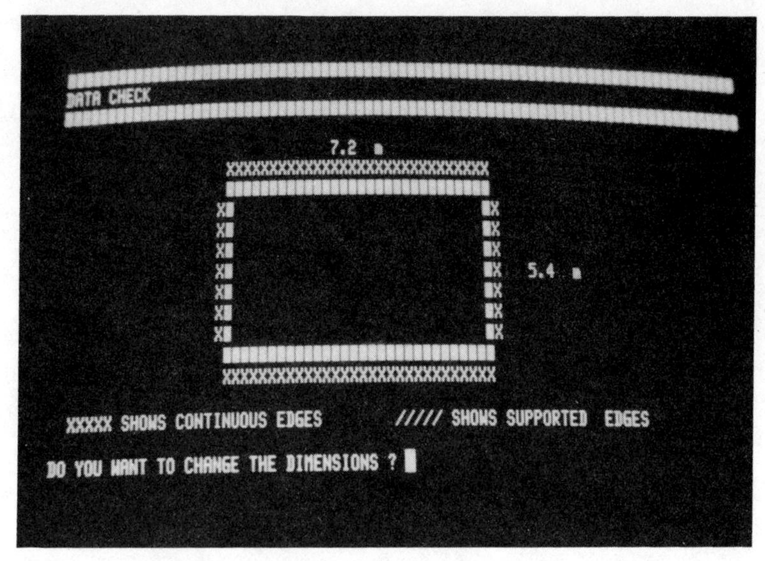

Fig. 3.13 Simple low resolution graphics display

block, and it is possible to draw graphs and relatively fine shapes. High resolution graphics requires a large amount of memory to store information on all pixels, and obviously the higher the resolution, the greater is the demand on memory. Graphics resolution varies between different micros, but typically between about 250 × 150 to 500 × 250 matrix of pixels. A black and white VDU using only one intensity of display would only require 1 bit to define whether the pixel is on or off, but for different intensities or different colours, more bits are required. The memory for graphics either has to be sacrificed from the 64K addressable memory (effectively reducing the amount of user RAM), or additional graphics memory (a 'graphics board') can be added to the micro to leave existing memory available for program or data use.

Micros with their own in-built graphics occupying part of the 64K RAM (for example, the Apple) will reduce the amount of RAM available for program space (for the reasons explained in Chapter 4). Some micros will not allow text graphics to be displayed at the same time because the VDU can only display the text memory window or the graphics memory window. Micros with additional graphics memory boards, for example the Intertec Superbrain, allow graphics and text displays to be overlaid on the VDU.

3.6.2 Hard-copy graphics

A graphical display developed on the VDU may ultimately be required on a hard-copy printout as shown in Fig. 3.14. The more usual way of producing this is to link either an 'X–Y' or 'Drum' plotter to the computer as shown in Fig. 3.15. An X–Y (sometimes called a 'flat-bed') plotter produces a paper copy using either single or

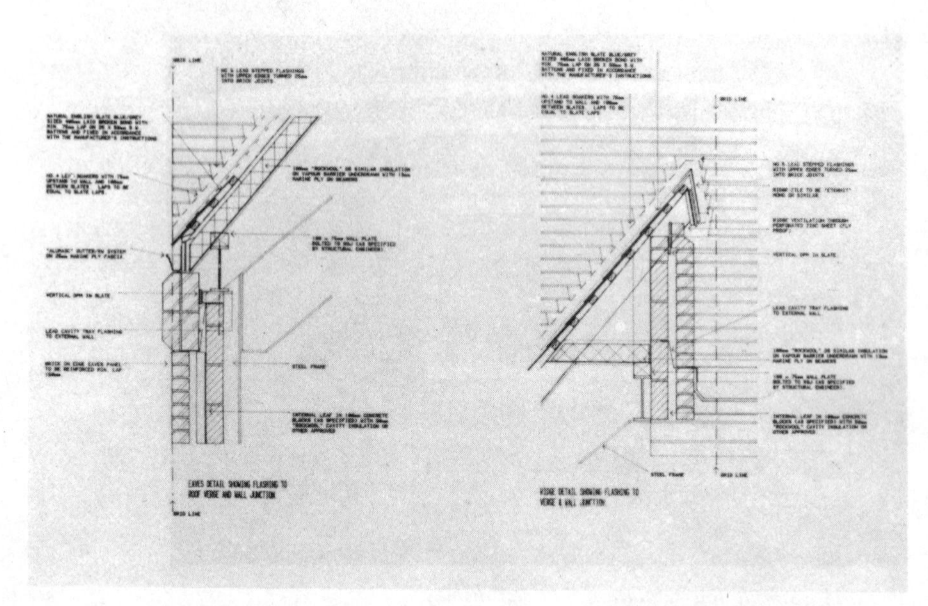

Fig. 3.14 High resolution graphics (courtesy of the Gable unit, Sheffield University)

Fig. 3.15 An X-Y plotter producing drawings up to A3 size (courtesy of the Gable unit, Sheffield University)

multiple pen sizes controlled in effect by movements between sets of co-ordinates. There are now a number of reasonably priced A4 and A3 size plotters available for use with microcomputers. Drum plotters tend to be more applicable for larger drawing sizes; the paper is wrapped around a drum which rotates in both directions about its axis, with multiple pen sizes moving in both directions parallel to the axis of rotation. Again, such plotters can be controlled by a micro, but a drum plotter is likely to be at least four or five times more expensive than the micro itself.

Although micros are capable of controlling plotters, each make of plotter will have its own unique set of plotter movement commands and these commands must be incorporated into an application program to produce the desired output. Most plotters will allow the program to control the resolution of the drawing (by controlling the size of step in the X and Y direction), the scale, automatic orientation and size of text, etc.

An alternative method of producing graphics can be to use the cheaper dot-matrix printers. Such printers use a single array of 7 or 9 needles each individually controllable by the user program. If the needle control codes are known, a simple graphical plot can be produced, for example, of a bending moment diagram or skeleton for a frame analysis as shown in Fig. 3.16. While the resolution is adequate for representation, scale drawings cannot be produced. Several commercial programs are available using this principle to produce a 'screen-dump' – an exact hard copy of a graphics display on a VDU.

3.6.3 Digitiser

An alternative to entering graphics through the keyboard is to use a digitiser. A digitiser is a means of transferring the co-ordinates of points on lines directly from a drawing or map to the computer using a hand-held cursor with a cross-hair as shown in Fig. 3.17 and input keys. Each digitiser manufacturer will use his own unique set of control codes and an application program will need to be able to recognise and interpret those codes.

Digitisers have been used with great effect for computerising road layouts, pipe networks, as well as the straightforward digitisation of standard construction drawings.

While the physical connection of digitisers and plotters is relatively straightforward, the same problems of communications protocol already described in section 3.5.3 arise. Again, we would recommend that the hardware supplier should ensure that the correct interfacing has been carried out.

3.7 A complete microcomputer system

With over 500 different makes of micro, a similar number of printers and the availability of all sorts of peripheral equipment, it is evident that there is no such thing as a typical microcomputer system. Although we shall discuss the approach to setting up a microcomputer system in Chapter 10, it is worth reviewing at this stage the range of systems available.

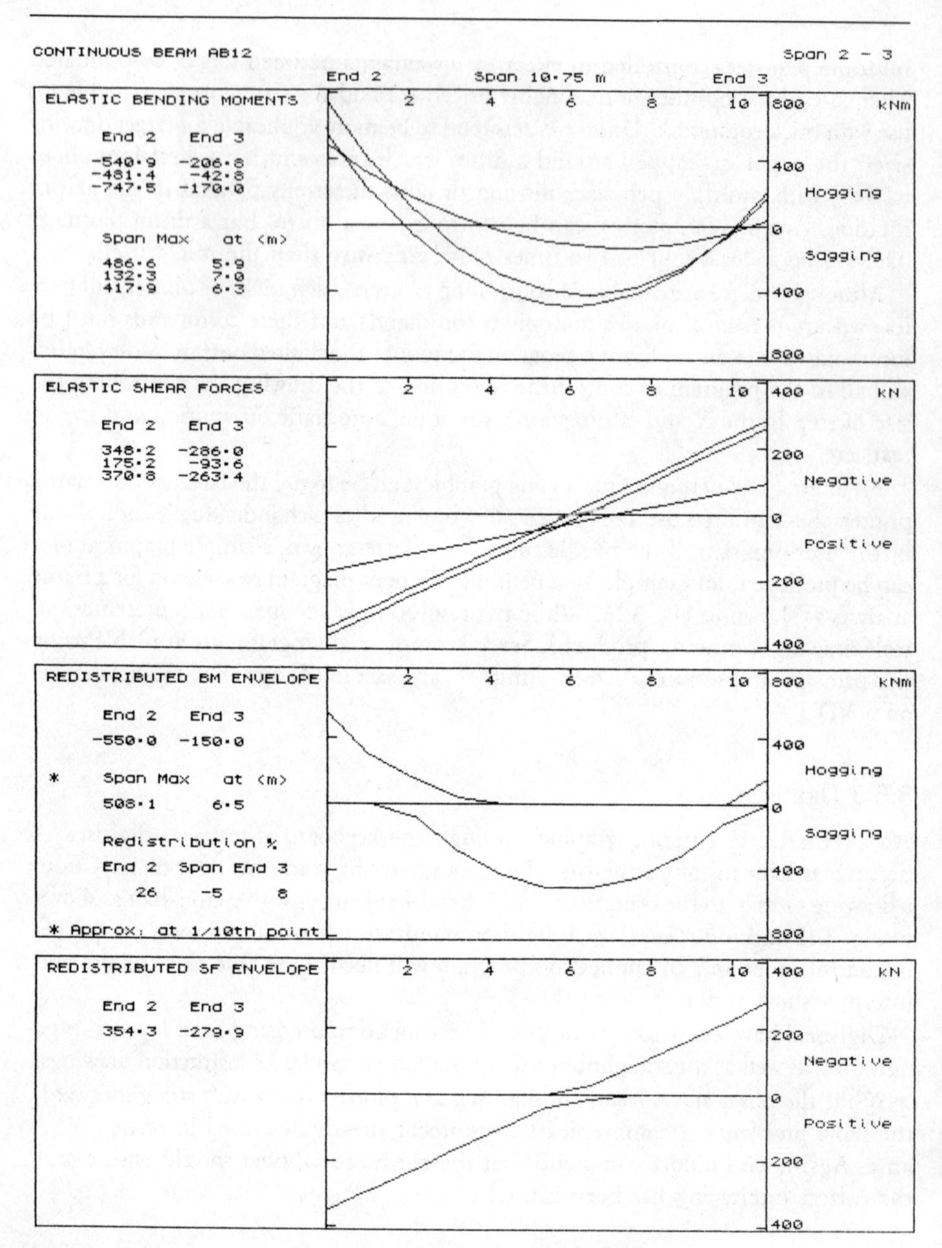

Fig. 3.16 Simple graphics printout from a dot matrix printer (courtesy of I. W. Burgess)

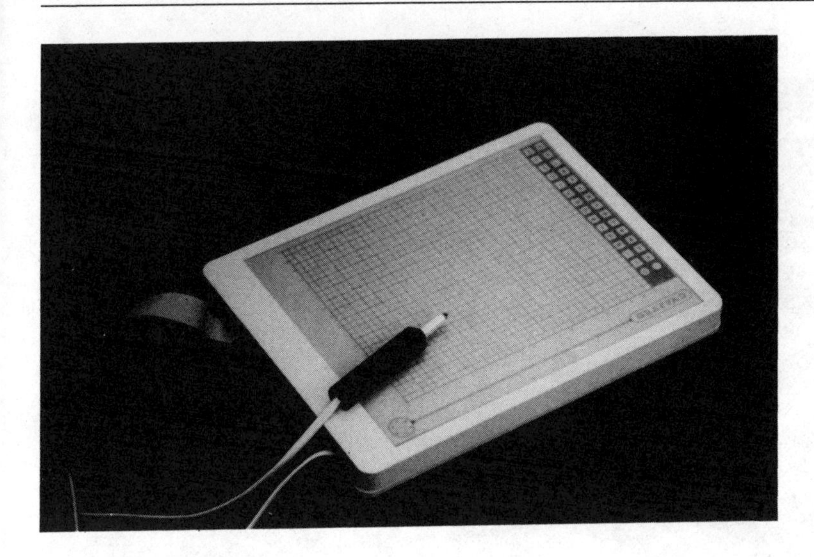

Fig. 3.17 A digitiser

3.7.1 Home computer system

At the low price end of the market there is an ever-changing range of home or hobbyist computers. While it is difficult to define a home computer, it is characterised by limited memory (say 8 – 64K), highly specific programming language and Operating System (the implications of which are discussed in Chapter 4), limited potential for expansion and mass storage which is unique to that computer. Although this may appear to be a damning indictment of home computers, they are in fact superb machines and are an excellent and cheap way to be introduced to computers. If the intention is to produce your own small design programs, a home computer system will achieve remarkable results. However, the biggest disadvantage is that if commercial design programs are to be purchased, there is an almost complete absence of good software available.

A typical home computer is the Sinclair Spectrum shown in Fig. 3.18. While the initial cost of such a micro is extremely low, it should be appreciated that if it is to be introduced into a design office and gradually expanded with a proper monitor, disc drives, printer, etc., the cost can increase dramatically. These considerations could make the purchase of a more expensive but more versatile micro a more attractive proposition.

3.7.2 Small business systems

In the mid-price range there are a number of systems which can be built up and expanded in modular form. The CPU, memory and keyboard may be in one unit, a separate VDU and separate disc drives connected when required, allowing a system to be expanded progressively. There is a tendency for such computers to have their own specific programming language and operating system, and design applications

Fig. 3.18 The Sinclair Spectrum — a typical home computer

Fig. 3.19 The Apple II – a typical small business computer

software may not be widely available. A typical system in this price range is the Apple as shown in Fig. 3.19, although for this micro (one of the first and most successful micros) there is a good range of analysis and design software available.

3.7.3 Standard professional system

Towards the top of the price range are the standard professional systems, characterised by almost identical specifications, available memory, disc configurations, interfacing capabilities, programming languages and operating system. Because of the similarities of specification, there is a considerably wider range of software available. In Chapter 4 we shall explain the significance of 'CP/M', but it is sufficient to say at this stage that because of the de facto standardisation of the CP/M operating system, programs developed on virtually any CP/M micro can be transferred to almost any other CP/M micro. This makes CP/M software available on an extremely wide range of computers. Examples of standard professional systems are numerous and even the larger computer manufacturers, ICL, IBM, DEC, Olivetti, etc., have produced micros (an example of which is shown in Fig. 3.20) which now use CP/M as an alternative to their own operating system. While CP/M has become the best-known operating system on 8-bit micros and, indeed, has been modified (CP/M–86) for the newer 16-bit micros, it now appears that MSDOS is becoming the accepted standard for 16-bit computers. From the point of view of the person using an applications program, there is very little practical difference between CP/M–86 and MSDOS, but the same point should be made, that standardisation of the operating system increases the probability of being able to transfer programs from one micro to another.

Fig. 3.20 The DEC Rainbow – a typical professional computer

Chapter 4

Computer system programs

In Chapter 3 we described the basic components of a microcomputer system. It is evident that there is a wide range of equipment available for the purchaser to tailor a system to his own requirements, but the hardware does not completely dictate the benefits of any particular system. The different components of a micro are controlled by an operating system and a user communicates with a micro via some form of programming language.

In this chapter we shall discuss the importance of the operating system and the alternative approaches to the selection of a programming language. We shall also discuss some of the additional facilities available on different micros. These features are collectively known as 'system programs' and should not be confused with 'applications' programs which are either written or purchased by a user.

4.1 Operating system

In Chapter 3 we referred to the 'monitor' program contained in ROM which comes into operation as soon as the computer is switched on; the monitor program is the lowest link between the user and the microprocessor and in some micros there may be no apparent evidence of its existence. All micros have their own operating system involving a complex program which can be thought of as the computer resource manager. In practice a user will probably want to perform a range of activities. For example, he may want to transfer a program from mass storage to RAM, to input or transfer data and to direct program responses or results to either the VDU, printer or mass storage. The organisation of the computer's resources is extremely complex and the main function of the operating system is to make the use of the computer as easy as possible.

The operating system does the same for simplifying the many different computer activities as the high-level language does for simplifying the input of a sequence of program instructions. Many aspects, from organising the way in which programs or data are stored on disc or cassette to the way in which the relevant peripheral is automatically accessed at the required time, are controlled by the operating system; this is under the control of the user by the issue of operating system commands. Such commands can be directed either through the keyboard or by the inclusion of appropriate statements in a high-level language program. The latter allows a program to read data automatically from a mass storage file, or to write results to a file or to a printer.

In the early days micros tended to have their own unique operating system which created problems of program and disc compatibility between different makes of micros and sometimes between different models of any one make. With time some operating systems were recognised as being better for the user and more efficient; de facto standards in the industry have gradually surfaced as a result of market forces. The most popular proprietary operating system for 8-bit micros is called CP/M (Control Program for Microcomputers, a trademark of Digital Research Inc.) which is now available on well over half of all micros with disc systems (DOC, 1980). Many of the manufacturers who originally developed their own operating system now recognise the benefits of CP/M and have either adopted that system or have made CP/M available as an option.

A vast software industry has flourished around the CP/M operating system. In theory, programs developed on one make of micro using CP/M will run on other makes of micro using CP/M. The laudable principle behind this standardisation is tarnished by problems of lack of compatibility of different disc systems, different visual display unit control codes, and for graphics systems, various graphics controls. It is not a straightforward task to transfer programs from one CP/M computer to another without a detailed knowledge of the two machines.

Since CP/M has become the standard operating system on 8-bit microcomputers, it is worth outlining how it is used. As stated earlier, the operating system of any micro organises the computer resources. CP/M does this both outside and inside application programs. Outside programs, CP/M provides a series of simple commands; for example:

DIR to display the names of all files on a disc.

STAT to display the names and sizes of all files and the amount of spare disc space.

PIP to transfer files from one disc to another, to copy files, to transmit or receive certain types of files to or from another computer.

ERA to erase specified disc files.

REN to rename a specified file.

In addition, there are many CP/M 'system programs' to allow new discs to be prepared to the format required by the computer, to set data transmission rates for communication with printers and other computers, to write assembly code programs, etc.

Inside programs, CP/M controls communication between the user, VDU, disc files and any other peripheral. Instructions to load or save a program, to record data on a disc file, to print data to a printer are interpreted and organised by CP/M. It should be emphasised that the user needs to know very little about CP/M; its very existence is to make computer operation as easy as possible.

The CP/M operating system is actually stored on disc and has to be loaded into the micro before it can be used – a process called 'booting the system'. When a typical CP/M micro is switched on the monitor program will either automatically attempt to read the operating system from a disc, or, if no disc has been inserted, it will display a message for a disc to be inserted. The operating system programs are automatically transferred from disc to RAM and remain there while the computer is being used.

It is obvious, therefore, that each separate disc to be used on the computer needs to have the operating system recorded on it. Because new discs can be used on any number of computers, they must each be prepared and have the operating system copied to them before they can be used for programs or data. Two CP/M programs are supplied (sometimes referred to as FORMAT and SYSGEN) for the process to be carried out.

While CP/M has dominated the 8-bit micro-operating systems, the greater availability of 16-bit micros has caused another operating system, MSDOS, to emerge as a new standard. Although CP/M is available in a 16-bit version (CP/M–86), many of the major micro manufacturers have selected MSDOS as a standard with CP/M–86 as an option. From a programmer's point of view, the differences are significant, but to a user the relative merits are so subtle as to make the two almost indistinguishable. For this reason we shall not discuss MSDOS in detail.

An industry standard operating system is the first step towards universal machine compatibility, although, as we have said, there are still many snags to be overcome before programs and data can be automatically transferred from one micro to another. The most important outstanding problem is the standardisation of mass storage media as discussed in Chapter 3.

4.2 High-level language

In Chapter 3 we described why the use of an assembly language is considerably better than machine-code programming, but there is no doubt that a 'high level' language is infinitely better. A high-level language enables the programmer to express his problem in a standardised and easily understood form which is almost independent of the microprocessor being used. Whereas a machine code or assembly language programmer would have to organise and specify his fetch-execute cycles and would have to control the memory system with a perfect knowledge of the internal workings of the microprocessor, a high-level language programmer can leave everything to the high-level language.

A high-level language uses program 'statements' which consist of readily understandable proper words and which contain standard scientific and arithmetic notation. Whereas machine code and assembly programs are written for the benefit and efficiency of the microprocessor, a high-level language is written for the convenience of the user. The structure of one particular high-level language will be presented in detail in Chapter 5, but knowledge of such a language is not required at this stage to understand how it is ultimately used by the microprocessor.

4.2.1 Interpreted languages

An 'interpreted' program language is translated one 'statement' or instruction at a time which is immediately executed by the computer before the next statement is translated. This is carried out by a language interpreter (a system program) which is contained in the micro.

The benefit of an interpreted program is that the program is actually running while the statements are being interpreted and both syntax errors (incorrect use of the language) and program logic or execution errors will be displayed immediately, usually with an error message describing why and where the error has occurred. The error can be corrected immediately and the program started again. However, interpreted programs are relatively slow to execute because of the step-wise interpretation of statements. Although this is not a real problem for many computer-aided design applications, it is a waste of computing capacity if one part of a program which is accessed many times has to be interpreted every time. A further disadvantage is that the language interpreter itself consumes user-RAM which, in a system using a compiled language (see section 4.2.2), would be available for a larger program or more data.

The most common interpreted high-level language on micros is BASIC which is described in detail in Chapter 5. BASIC was originally developed at Dartmouth College in the United States for use in the teaching of computer programming. Unlike most other standard languages, BASIC suffers from not having a universally standard form. Indeed, BASIC can vary from a variety of small or 'Integer' BASICs to very sophisticated 'extended' BASICs. The form, logic and structure of the different varieties is common, but specific features vary considerably. Some micros have their high-level language interpreter stored permanently in ROM while others require the language to be loaded into RAM. Either way, the language requires a certain amount of addressable memory and while there are many programming benefits of using an extended BASIC, there may be penalties of loss of user-RAM. For example, a simple BASIC may require only about 2K of memory, but is limited to very simple arithmetic operations, while an extended BASIC may require about 30K of memory, and may not leave the user with very much RAM with which to use the extra facilities offered.

The range of BASIC languages obviously gives the buyer some scope to select a language to suit the requirements of his system, but one of the most inconvenient aspects of this choice is that it is not easy to transfer a BASIC program developed on one make of micro to any other make. In practice there are several ways of overcoming this problem and, as the micro industry sorts itself out, certain versions of BASIC will gradually become de facto industry standards.

Micros with BASIC in ROM tend to be those with their own particular dialect of language. Because the language has been implanted on an integrated circuit, the only way to change the language (for example to accommodate improved language versions) is to replace the circuit. However, micros using BASIC loaded by the user into RAM are considerably more versatile because, as language enhancements become available, a disc or tape copy of the new language can be purchased and loaded into RAM without having to change any circuitry. Such micros can therefore take advantage of any standardisation of BASIC languages that will inevitably occur in the future. Indeed, some degree of standardisation is occurring by the wider acceptance of Microsoft BASIC (or MBASIC) which is now available on many micros with the language loaded into RAM. Of course, the disadvantage of BASIC in RAM is that the language has to be loaded into memory by the user before it can be used.

4.2.2 Compiled languages

A 'compiled' language is a high-level language program which has been translated into machine code (the 'compiled' program) before the program is actually used. The compiled program can be stored in a mass storage device and can then be loaded and run on any number of occasions. The beauty of a compiled program is that, being in machine code, it will run quickly and it uses memory space economically. However, the compilation process can be slow and frustrating; a program under development must first be compiled and, although the compiler checks the syntax of the language, the program logic and arithmetic accuracy cannot be checked until the compiled program is run. Any errors would have to be corrected in the high-level language and the program compiled and run again before detecting any further errors. This process can be exhausting, particularly bearing in mind that the compiler itself can be large and memory-demanding and can take a considerable amount of time converting the user's program into machine code.

FORTRAN, PASCAL and COBOL are all examples of compiled programming languages, all of which are available on micros. If we are to develop our own applications program, a language using a compiler is not totally satisfactory. If, however, a standard (and proven) compiled applications program is to be purchased, there are considerable benefits of being able to use a faster and less memory-demanding compiled program.

4.2.3 Compilable-interpreted languages

An obvious compromise to take advantage of the benefits of both interpreted and compiled languages is a language which allows a program to be developed with an interpreter and, when perfected, then to be compiled. Microsoft BASIC (MBASIC), which is available on a number of micros using the CP/M operating system, allows exactly this facility. Programs are written, entered, tested and corrected with the normal benefits of an interpreted language and, when completed, can be compiled to take advantage of considerably faster processing time and the release of additional memory.

The compiling process is relatively straightforward, the only hurdle being the jargon. The program to be compiled (the 'source' program) has to go through two processes, first to produce relocatable object code, and second to produce the final compiled codes. There is little point in explaining the details of these processes except to say that the first stage will completely check the syntax of the source program – a very useful aid for the programmer.

The only danger to be aware of is that there are a few subtle differences between interpreted and compiled MBASIC. The most important is that arrays must be fully dimensioned and cannot be re-dimensioned in compiled programs whereas, in interpreted MBASIC, arrays can vary in size and can be re-dimensioned. This is because the compiler must reserve array space at the compilation stage, not at the time of program execution.

4.2.4 Other high-level languages

Although BASIC is the most popular high-level language used on micros, its main disadvantage is the variety of dialects available. Many hundreds of different high-level languages have been written over the years – Sammet (1976) reported 167 different languages still in use in America in 1974–5, but there are only a few universally standardised languages – FORTRAN, ALGOL, COBOL, PASCAL, etc., many of which have been associated with mainframe computers. Indeed, the very reason for the success of these languages was that companies such as IBM developed and adopted the languages as support for their hardware. FORTRAN is now about 25 years old and its de facto standardisation and continuing acceptance within the scientific and engineering world is as much due to the very high investment already made in program writing as to conservatism or resistance to change (Jackson, 1980). Although FORTRAN has been enhanced during its lifetime, its standardisation and appropriateness to engineering applications has made it the standard language within the civil and structural engineering sector for use on mainframe and minicomputers.

FORTRAN is available as an alternative to BASIC on many microcomputers, but it is a compiled, not an interpreted, language. The relative advantages of compiled programs have already been discussed in this chapter, but there is a further benefit of FORTRAN which is often promoted, albeit one which we would question. It is frequently claimed that by using FORTRAN it is relatively easy to down-grade existing mainframe programs for use on a microcomputer. Without trying to pre-empt our line of reasoning in later chapters, it is worth bearing in mind that existing mainframe programs are not usually the type that we would want to use in day-to-day computer-aided design.

It is worth noting that FORTRAN subroutines to carry out standard procedures (for example, matrix inversion) may in many cases be linked with a compiled BASIC program. Obviously, the combined languages cannot be tested until the program is actually compiled and used, but linking of the different languages does overcome the problems of translating parts of favourite and well-tested FORTRAN programs into BASIC.

4.3 Numerical accuracy

It is often assumed that computers are 'extremely accurate'; indeed, one reason for using a computer is because good accuracy in a calculation is essential. The numerical accuracy of different high-level languages unfortunately varies considerably. At the lowest level a Tiny or Integer BASIC can only deal with integer numbers; although it is possible to divide one number by another, the result will be truncated to an integer value. The reason that such languages exist is because a considerable amount of memory is saved by working only in integers. Obviously, there is a trade-off between complex numerical accuracy and speed of computation. The reality of numerical accuracy lies first in the number of significant figures in the result of a calculation and second in the form and extent of approximation used to derive some standard functions.

The number of significant figures in a number is limited by the maximum number of bytes available to store the number in memory. Many languages on cheaper micros use between seven and nine significant figures, while more expensive micros sometimes use a language with perhaps only six significant figures. We shall see in Chapter 5 that in BASIC it is possible to specify standard trigonometrical functions (sine, cosine, etc.) which are calculated by a series approximation. The accuracy of the function is obviously determined by the number of terms assumed in the series and by the number of significant figures in its calculated value. For most civil and structural engineering applications we shall not be too concerned about deriving an answer which is correct to a large number of significant figures. Indeed, the thought of calculating a concrete stress to any more than integer accuracy would be naive in view of the many other broad assumptions in concrete design. However, there is one particular field of application where considerable numerical accuracy is essential, and that is in the use of co-ordinate geometry in surveying, highway alignment design, etc. For example, a combination of Ordnance Survey grid references, often involving nine digit numbers and trigonometrical functions limited to seven significant figures can cause serious rounding errors. If a micro is to be used for such applications it is essential to find a programming language which provides sufficient numerical accuracy or, as is now more common, to use a language which has the facility for 'double precision' calculations working to about fourteen significant figures.

As mentioned in Chapter 3, numbers can be specified as integer, single or double precision. Using Microsoft BASIC (MBASIC), Table 4.1 shows the memory requirements, significance and maximum and minimum values for the different numerical precisions.

Table 4.1 Memory requirements, significance and maximum and minimum values related to numerical precision

	Storage requirement (bytes)	Significant digits	Minimum value	Maximum value
Integer	2	5	−32767	+32767
Single precision	4	7	-10^{-38}	10^{+38}
Double precision	8	16	-10^{-38}	10^{+38}

It is evident that if certain variables are known to be of integer value only, it is worth specifying those variables as integers which require only half the memory of single precision variables.

4.4 Graphics

In Chapter 3 we discussed the hardware implications of graphics. In this section we shall consider the software requirements to control graphics displays.

4.4.1 Low resolution graphics

As already discussed in Chapter 3, low resolution graphics involves the arrangement of standard keyboard characters on the VDU display, usually with a resolution of about 80 × 24, depending on the particular micro.

No special language is required to produce such displays; the normal programming commands will allow individual characters to be displayed at specified positions on the VDU. Using a series of X–Y screen co-ordinates it is relatively easy to produce simple diagrams or histograms. Printing low resolution graphics on a printer is a little more complicated because most printers do not allow a reverse paper feed, but only a little thought is required to devise ways of producing histograms on a printer using normal print commands, or as shown in Fig. 4.1 to produce an earthworks mass-haul diagram.

4.4.2 High resolution graphics

Unlike low resolution graphics, high resolution graphics requires a special version of the high level language which includes additional commands to control the graphics display. The commands will be of the form PLOT (X1, Y1, X2, Y2, I) which means 'plot a line of intensity I from screen co-ordinates X1,Y1 to co-ordinates X2,Y2'. Many additional commands will allow complex drawings to be developed in different intensities of brightness and with various shadings.

Although the facility to produce graphics is a very acceptable feature, it should be appreciated that both graphics hardware and software are likely to be specific to the micro being used and the opportunities to transfer applications programs to or from other micros will be severely limited. In addition, if the micro has in-built graphics in its 64K memory (as distinct from an additional graphics board), there will be substantial loss of user-RAM.

4.5 Use of memory

The problems of fitting all features provided by a micro into its available memory can now be brought together and explained in terms of a 'memory map'.

For convenience we shall use as an example the memory system of the highly successful Apple II micro. The Apple uses an 8-bit byte and 16-bit (2-byte) address

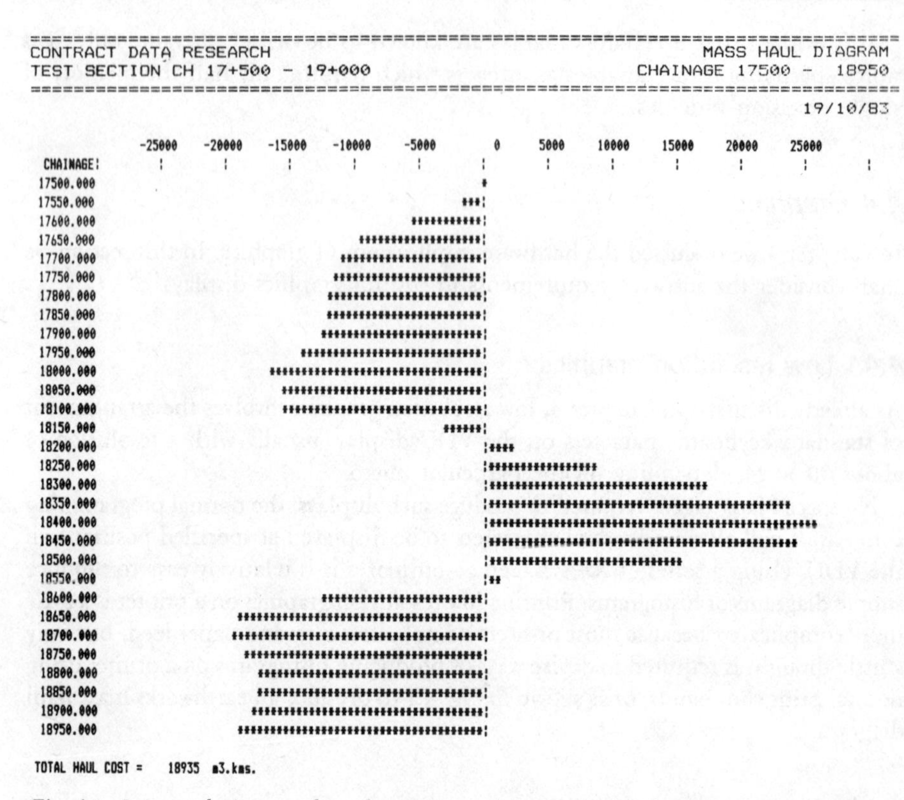

Fig. 4.1 Low resolution graphics characters used to print an earthworks mass-haul diagram. (courtesy of Contract Data Research)

bus. For the reasons explained in Chapter 3, the Apple therefore has a 64K addressing capability. Although details of the Apple memory organisation are very specific to the Apple the same principles are used in other micros.

All memory can be shown as a stack or memory map with memory location 0 at the bottom and location 65 535 at the top. For simplicity, we shall reference all memory to its nearest K (the nearest 1 024 bytes); the bottom of the map will therefore be 0K and the top will 64K.

Figure 4.2 (a) shows an empty memory map with 64K capable of being addressed. In the Apple there is some RAM and a considerable amount of ROM dedicated to particular functions. As shown in Fig. 4.2 (b), the memory between 0 and 2K is RAM reserved to operate the keyboard and VDU, and the memory between 48K and 64K is ROM reserved to control the monitor program, input and output and the BASIC language interpreter. This leaves 46K spare for program or data.

A user's program starts in RAM at 2K and fills memory 'upwards' towards 46K. However, any data produced by the program is stored in RAM at 46K and fills memory 'downwards'. There obviously may come a point at which the top of a large program and the bottom of large amounts of data will meet, resulting in an 'OUT OF MEMORY' error which is the fear of all microcomputer programmers. There is little alternative except to reduce the program or data size to enable the program to operate successfully.

The system shown in Fig. 4.2 (b) is for a tape backup system. If a disc system is incorporated, the operating system consumes the RAM between about 38K and 48K. As shown in Fig. 4.2 (c), this reduces further the amount of user RAM because the top of the data memory is pushed down to 38K, reducing user-RAM significantly to 36K. For comparison, a 64K micro with the CP/M operating system and the more complex MBASIC interpreter provides only about 28K of user-RAM.

While user-RAM therefore reduces the total addressable memory by one half it should be appreciated that it can still accommodate a program of about 1 000 statements (but no reserved data space).

As discussed in Chapter 3 and earlier in this chapter, micros with built-in graphics will reduce user-RAM even more. The Apple has two areas of RAM which can be reserved for graphics. The action of reserving these areas has the effect of preventing that RAM from being used for program storage.

Figure 4.2 (d) shows the memory map with the reserved graphics areas between 8K and 16K and between 16K and 24K. If the 8K to 16K graphics area is reserved, it is evident that an application program is limited to a total of 6K but data can be a total of 22K, whilst, if the 16K to 24K graphics area is reserved, the maximum program size increases to 14K and data space reduces to 14K.

The main purpose of describing the memory map in detail is to provide some guidance on how to interpret sales specifications. Whereas the Apple is a very useful system because of the availability of high resolution graphics, the point needs to be made that a total of only 64K addressable memory is available in an 8-bit micro and the additional features of one system compared with another will have been provided at the expense of other features. It is therefore important that the buyer should be aware of the swings and roundabouts. It is unfortunate that micro

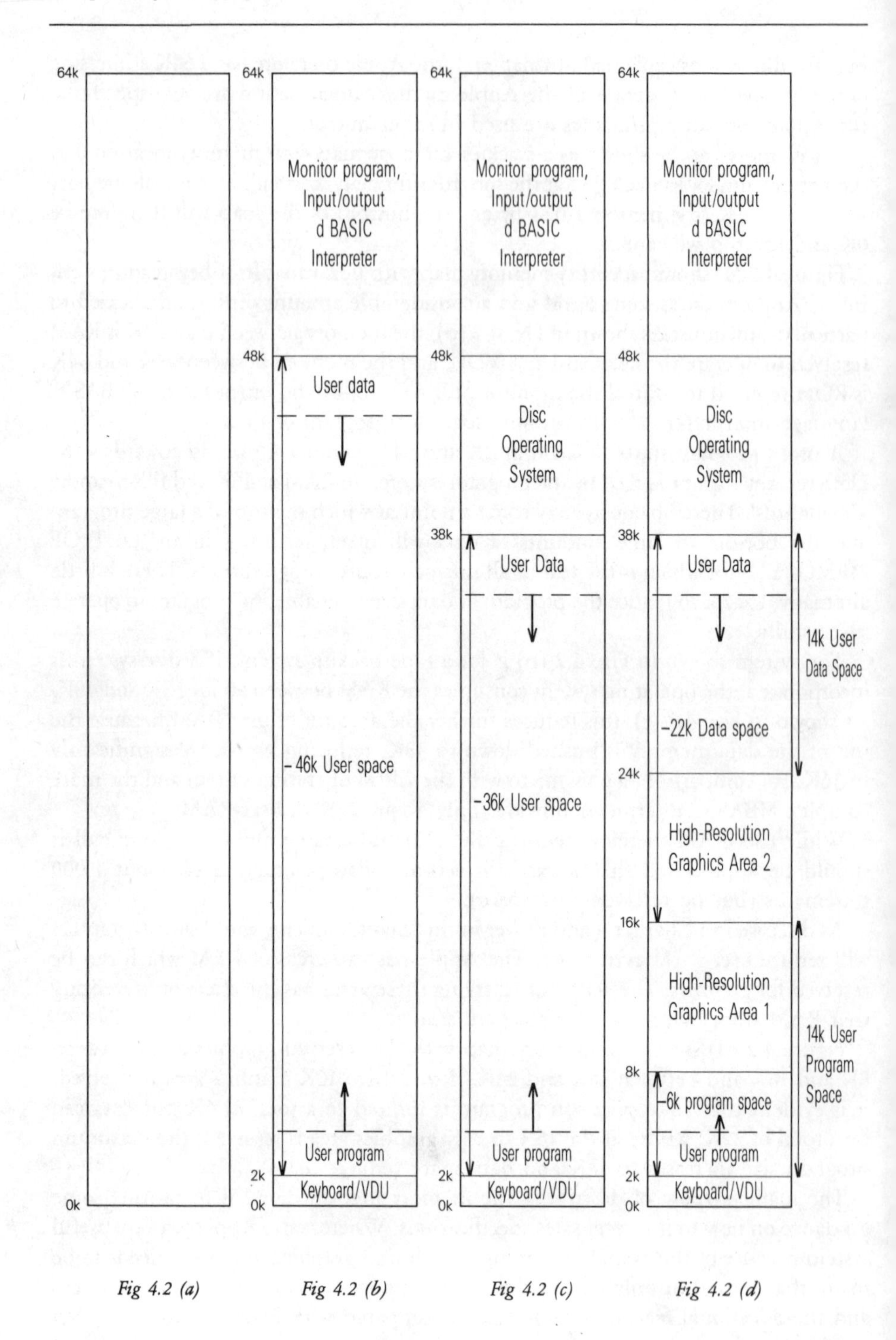

Fig. 4.2 Apple II memory allocation map

manufacturers are unable to standardise their specification of user-RAM. On first sight a system advertised as a 64K micro appears to be better than a 48K micro at the same price. The 64K micro system obviously refers to the total addressing capability, whereas the 48K system may refer to user-RAM without a disc operating system. Although it is easy to criticise the variety of ways of quoting the capacity of the system, the difficulties of adopting a standard method must be appreciated.

In this chapter we have discussed how the operating system, programming language, numerical accuracy and additional graphics facilities are combined together to produce a system ready to use for application programs. We shall now proceed to see how such a system can best be used.

Chapter 5

Computer programming

It is not the intention in this chapter to teach the reader how to write a complicated program; indeed, there are many excellent books better suited to that task and most microcomputers are supplied with a detailed reference manual on the particular language used. However, for readers with little or no knowledge of computer programs, an introduction to one particular programming language is essential in preparation for subsequent chapters. The language to be used is BASIC – an acronym for Beginners' All-purpose Symbolic Instruction Code. It is unfortunate that the word 'Beginners' was used to form the acronym because BASIC is a very powerful general purpose scientific programming language suitable for application in almost all analysis and design applications. Whereas other more powerful languages are available on some microcomputers (FORTRAN, ALGOL, PASCAL, etc.), their additional features are often associated with greater language complexity and a loss of flexibility. BASIC is widely available although there may be variations between implementations on different microcomputers. The fundamentals of BASIC described in this chapter will be applicable to most versions of the language, although the examples we quote refer to MBASIC.

Whilst the general features of BASIC may be appreciated from the examples given in this chapter, the reader will learn considerably more if the examples are tried out on a micro at the same time as reading the text. The best way to learn programming is to do it.

5.1 What is a language?

Before discussing the use of BASIC it is worthwhile considering what is required of any language, whether a spoken language or a computer language. A conventional language is simply a method of communication between at least two people who accept the same rules of vocabulary and grammar. The principle of a programming language is the same except that the communication is between a person and a machine. However, the similarity ends here, because although communication between people can tolerate a certain degree of incorrect grammar or ambiguous vocabulary, a computer only accepts the absolutely perfect use of the language. The success of a computer language therefore depends on establishing a set of rules and identifying a unique vocabulary, preferably using words which are vaguely similar to the user's normal language. Because the rules are so rigid, a good computer language will use as few words as possible, thereby reducing the risk of ambiguity.

5.2 The rules of BASIC

The rules of BASIC are simple; depending on the particular version of BASIC being used, there will be about 50 'reserved words' or symbols which will make the computer perform particular operations. Instructions are made by setting out these reserved words in a specific format and in a logical sequence. Most words are the same as, or abbreviations of, English words and many of the symbols are similar to conventional arithmetic notation.

As a simple example of a program, consider a 3 m beam simply supported at its ends with a load of 6 kN uniformly distributed over its entire length. The bending moment M at any point X from a support is given in normal arithmetic notation by:

$$M = X(3 - X)$$

If we require a program to calculate M at any point X then the program instruction:

```
M=X*(3-X)
```

is a valid instruction because the computer recognises that '*' means multiply, '−' means subtract and '( )' means that everything inside the brackets must be evaluated first before multiplying by X. The symbols M and X are not reserved words and, because of their context, they are assumed to be the 'names' of variables. However, the instruction to calculate M cannot be obeyed until a value of X has been given, and the results for M cannot be communicated by the computer until the appropriate instructions are given.

The following is a complete program to give M for a given value of X:

```
10 INPUT X
20 M=X*(3-X)
30 PRINT M
40 END
```

This simple program demonstrates some fundamental BASIC rules. First, every instruction (which hereafter will be referred to as a program 'statement') must be numbered in ascending order to show the sequence in which the statements are to be processed. Statement numbers may start at any positive number and may be spaced by any interval, but it is good practice to step statement numbers by at least 10 to allow the insertion of additional statements at a later stage. The order in which the statements are entered into the computer is totally flexible; statement 20 could be entered before 10 and the micro will automatically sort and display the statements in the correct order.

Second, the special words INPUT and PRINT are used to instruct the computer to request a value of X and to print the result M. These are reserved words and must be exact; the words IN PUT and PRIN T would not be recognised and an error would appear on attempting to run the program. This is normally called a 'Syntax' error because it violates the strict rules of the language's grammar.

Third, because X and M are not reserved words and because of their position in relation to '=', it is assumed by the computer that they are the 'names' of numeric variables and their values will be assigned to an appropriate memory location. The number of characters defining a numeric variable varies between different microcomputers. In general, a one- or two-digit word (the one or first digit being a letter and the second a letter or number) may be used to name a variable. Thus, A, AA, A5, GT, Z7 are all valid variable names. In statement 10 of the above program the value given in response to INPUT X would be stored in the memory location for X and all future references to X would use that stored value unless it had been assigned a new value by a subsequent statement. Similarly, in line 20 the value in the memory location for M will be given the result of X*(3−X), and it is this value which is automatically retrieved from memory and printed in line 30. It should be noted that if a variable is used without having a value assigned to it, its value will be assumed to be zero.

A final rule is that all programs should contain an END statement to tell the computer that the end of the program has been reached.

5.3 More on arithmetic statements

Although most of the arithmetic work in a program is similar to normal algebraic notation, there are some peculiarities. For example:

```
10 M=M*2
```

is a valid statement although algebraically it looks incorrect. This statement is a 'reassignment' of the variable M because, in effect, it is saying 'Store in the memory location for M the existing value for M multiplied by 2'. The general rule is that where an '=' occurs in an expression, the variable on the left-hand side will be given a new value as defined by the result of the right-hand side. However, some conventional algebraic equations such as:

$$2A=B+C$$

cannot be represented directly to calculate A because the left-hand side must be a variable name, not a mathematical sequence. Such equations can usually be re-written in such a way that the example above becomes:

$$A=(B+C)/2$$

Almost any mathematical expression may be programmed in BASIC using the standard principles of algebra and using any of the following arithmetic 'operators':

+ add	/ divide
− subtract	∧ raise to the power of
* multiply	

Mathematical expressions may be 'nested' by the use of brackets, the rule being that the expression in the innermost set of brackets will always be calculated first. The sequence of calculation using operators follows fairly rigid rules yet allows brackets to override; ∧ will be calculated first, then * or /, then + or −.

As an example of more complicated arithmetic statements, and to provide a common example for the following sections, consider the general problem of a beam of length L metres, simply supported at its ends with a load W kN uniformly distributed along its entire length as shown in Fig. 5.1.

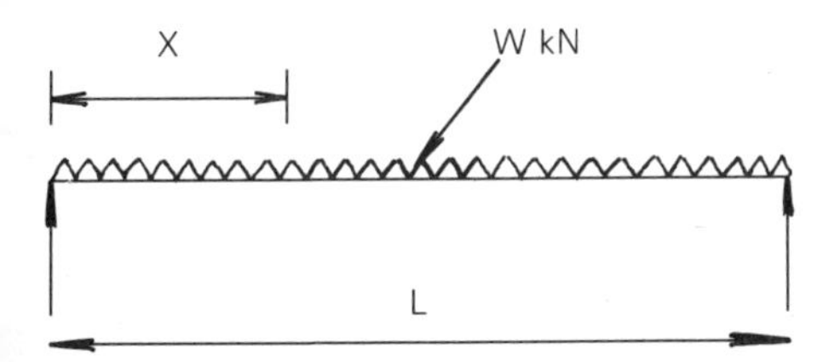

Fig. 5.1 Example problem of a simply supported beam with a UDL

At any point X on the beam:

$$\text{Bending moment } M = \frac{WX(L-X)}{2L} \text{ kNm}$$

$$\text{and Deflection } D = \frac{WX(L^3 - 2LX^2 + X^3) * 10^{12}}{24EIL} \text{ mm}$$

where E = modulus of elasticity (N/mm^2)

and I = second moment of area (mm^4)

These equations can be written in BASIC as:

```
230 M=W*X*(L-X)/(2*L)
240 D=W*X*(L∧3-2*L*X∧2+X∧3)*1E12/(24*E*I*L)
```

The statement numbers in these and subsequent statements have been chosen to develop a complete program shown towards the end of this chapter. Where examples of statements are given which are not to be included in the final program, no statement number will be used.

Notice that 2*L and 24*E*I*L have been bracketed together so that the numerator will be divided by the whole of the denominator and not by 2 or 24 and the answer then multiplied by L or E*I*L. A good rule is always to use brackets if there is any doubt at all. Also, exponential notation can be used to represent large numbers as in 1E12 representing 10^{12}.

5.4 Functions

In addition to the standard operators, BASIC always has some built-in 'functions'. The more common functions are:

SIN(X) : Sine of X
COS(X) : Cosine of X
TAN(X) : Tangent of X
ATN(X) : Arctangent of X ($\tan^{-1}$ of X)
ABS(X) : Absolute value of X
INT(X) : Highest integer less than or equal to X
LOG(X) : Natural logarithm of X
SQR(X) : Square root of X (same as X∧0.5)
RND(X) : Random number 'seeded' by X (varies between different versions of BASIC)

Each of these functions can be included in an arithmetic statement. For example, the angle in radians subtended by a chord of length L in a circle of radius R could be calculated by:

```
T=2*ATN(L/2/SQR(R∧2-(L/2)∧2))
```

5.5 The conditional test

The sequence in which a program must run cannot always be determined until at least some of the program statements have been executed and certain conditions have been tested and satisfied. In the beam problem it may be necessary to check that the maximum deflection is within certain limits before proceeding with the calculation of bending moments, and on the basis of this check to use a specified value of I or give the user the opportunity to try a new value of I. This can be achieved with a 'conditional test' using the IF...THEN statement. For example, if the maximum deflection is greater than L/360, i.e.

$$\text{if } \frac{5WL^3 \times 10^{12}}{384EI} \text{ is greater than } \frac{L}{0.36}$$

then the program should stop and ask for a new value of I. This can be programmed as:

```
170 IF 5*W*L∧3*1E12/(384*E*I)>(L/0.36 THEN GOTO 300
```

The words IF and THEN are reserved words. The IF statement compares the arithmetic expressions and if the result is found to be true the operation following THEN is carried out. In line 170 the operation following THEN transfers control to line 300. If the comparison is found to be false, the operation following THEN would be ignored and the next statement would be executed. An IF...THEN statement must contain one of the following:

=	is equal to
<	is less than
>	is greater than
<=	is less than or equal to
>=	is greater than or equal to
< >	is not equal to

The instruction following THEN may be a statement in itself; for example, the printing of a message, a calculation or a command for the program to stop.

5.6 The unconditional transfer

A transfer to any point (forwards or backwards) in a program may also be made using the GOTO statement. This is an unconditional transfer – it does not depend on the outcome of a test. The statement:

```
340 GOTO 310
```

has been used in the beam problem for reasons to be explained later.

5.7 Program loops

Many problems require the repetitive use of the same statements using different values of variables. If the number of repetitions is known, a 'program loop' can be used with FOR...NEXT statements. The general form for a program loop is:

```
FOR A=J TO K STEP L
...
...
...
NEXT A
```

where J, K and L are constants or known variables. This instruction causes the statements between FOR and NEXT to be executed a number of times determined by the number of steps of size L in the difference between J and K. In many program loops the steps will be unity, in which case STEP 1 may be omitted. It should be noted that a FOR...NEXT loop is always executed at least once.

A program loop can be used in the beam problem to calculate the bending moments and deflections at increments of L/10 along the beam; this would produce sufficient data to plot the bending moment diagram and a deflection profile. The following:

```
220 FOR X=0 TO L STEP L/10
...
... Statements to calculate and print M and D
...
260 NEXT X
```

would go through 11 iterations using the same statements (230 to 250) to calculate and print new values of M and D for each new value of X. On the first iteration X would take the value 0, for the second iteration it would be 0+L/10, in the next iteration it would be 0+2L/10 and so on until the final iteration when X would take the value L.

Program loops may be nested one inside the other to any reasonable level and although it is possible to jump out of a loop using a conditional transfer (IF...THEN), it is impossible to jump into the middle of a loop without going through the appropriate FOR statement.

5.8 Subroutines

Subroutines are usually self-contained parts of a program which require frequent access from different points in the main part of the program. Although not absolutely essential, subroutines improve the structure of a program by making it more modular. A subroutine is 'called' by GOSUB n, where n is a statement number, and the immediate effect is the same as GOTO n. The advantage of GOSUB is that at the end of a subroutine there has to be a RETURN statement which will cause program execution to return to the line immediately following the calling GOSUB statement.

Subroutines are used to best advantage in larger programs and an example of their use in the beam program will not therefore be given, although reference to subroutines will be made in subsequent chapters.

5.9 Input and output

The preceding sections have dealt almost exclusively with arithmetic operations in which data have been manipulated to produce the desired answers. In discussing these operations it has been assumed that the data (the values of L, W, E, I, etc.) are already stored for use by the computer. Although it may be of no consolation to the reader at this stage, it should be noted that programming the arithmetic part of a program is considerably easier to learn than the control of data input and output. The following sections will show how data can be requested and the results displayed by program statements.

5.10 Data input through the keyboard

The INPUT statement is used when the program requires data to be entered by the user through the computer keyboard. Earlier in the chapter we saw the simplest form of INPUT statement as:

```
INPUT X
```

When this statement is reached the program stops and waits for the appropriate numeric value to be keyed in. The value given by the user is automatically stored in the memory location for X and is used in all subsequent statements involving X until superseded by a reassigned value of X.

The INPUT statement is more versatile than this because a certain amount of 'prompting' text may be displayed to tell the user exactly what is being requested. Returning to the beam problem, the values of L, E, W, and I have to be entered; for example, to enter the value of I this can be achieved with text prompts as follows:

```
150 INPUT "ENTER SECOND MOMENT OF AREA (MM^4)"; I
```

The prompt is all text between the two quotation marks and the variable name I is usually (depending on the version of BASIC) separated from the prompt by a semicolon. When line 150 is reached in the program the prompt will be displayed to inform the user what is being requested and the program will wait until a value is given for I. Similar prompted INPUT statements may be used for the other beam variables.

One INPUT statement may also be used to request values for a number of variables as in:

```
INPUT A, B, C, D, E
```

The user must enter five values, each separated by a comma, before the program will continue to the next statement. In many versions of BASIC, if only one value is input the computer will continue to request additional data until a sufficient number of values has been given to satisfy the number of variables in the INPUT statement.

5.11 The use of constant data

If the same data is to be used every time the program is run, the data may be included in DATA statements which are read automatically by READ statements. The DATA statements may be positioned anywhere in a program. When the first READ statement is encountered on executing the program, the value contained in the first DATA statement is assigned to the appropriate variable name. The subsequent READ statement uses the value of the next DATA statement, and so on. For example, if the beam problem always uses the same value for L and W (which will not be so in our case) then:

```
READ L, W
DATA 3.5, 2.7
```

would automatically assign the value of 3.5 to L and 2.7 to W, as would:

```
READ L
READ W
DATA 3.5, 2.7
```

It is therefore essential that data is in the exact order in which it is to be read by the READ statement.

5.12 Printing results

PRINT is used to convey information or results to the user. Printing is carried out either on the VDU or, if required, on to a printer. Of all BASIC statements PRINT varies the most from one version to another.

The value of a variable (for example, variable X) can be printed (i.e. displayed on the VDU) using the straightforward:

```
PRINT X
```

and its value would be displayed on the left-hand side of the VDU.

As with the INPUT statement PRINT can use a combination of text and variable. For example:

```
PRINT "THE VALUE OF X = ";X
```

would display the text between the quotation marks followed by the stored value of X. Again, the text and variable are usually separated by a semicolon.

A PRINT statement may print several values on the same line using:

```
PRINT A, B, C
```

The commas separating the variables are significant because they are used to fix the position for printing B and C (A is printed at the left-hand margin) at tabulation positions depending on the particular type of computer being used. Most microcomputers have 3 or 4 tabulation points across the row or paper printout and each comma in a PRINT statement causes the printing of the next variable to occur at the next tabulation point. This could be useful for tabulating results in columns. By using semicolons instead of commas the tabulation would be suppressed and the printing of the next variable would follow the end of the previous variable.

Returning again to the beam problem, the results of M and D are printed for each position of X along the beam by using the following in the previously discussed FOR...NEXT loop:

```
250 PRINT X, M, D
```

It should be noted that if any text had been included in this statement then it would be printed as many times as the number of iterations in the FOR...NEXT loop. Since this would not make an attractive display, it is worth including PRINT statements before the loop starts to produce headings for the columns of results, as in:

```
190 PRINT "X", "B.M.", "DEFLECTION"
200 PRINT "(M)", "(KNM)", "(MM)"
```

Another PRINT statement is required in the beam problem to produce an error message if the maximum deflection exceeds L/360, as follows:

```
300 PRINT "MAXIMUM DEFLECTION > L/360"
```

5.13 More on variables

The variables used in the examples so far have been numeric variables and have been assumed to have 'real' values (decimal numbers). BASIC also allows variables to be defined as 'integers' (whole numbers) or as 'strings' (text). An integer normally has a % following its variable name and although it provides some saving in memory space (see Chapter 3 and section 8.6) its use is not worth pursuing in detail. String variables are identified by a $ after the variable name. By default, if neither a % nor a $ follows a variable name it is assumed to be a real variable. This means that the variables:

```
X, X%, X$
```

are each unique variables and will be stored in different registers although they each use the same letter to define the name. Some versions of BASIC also allow variables to be defined as 'double precision' (see section 4.3).

String variables are very useful because, although they consist of text, some of the conditional tests may be used to compare different strings, and two or more string variables may be joined together to form a larger string variable. This, in fact, is the basis of how microcomputers may be used as word processors.

5.14 String variables

A value is assigned to a string variable using the usual = and the string of text is enclosed by quotation marks, as in:

```
A$="SHEAR FORCE"
```

This stores the words SHEAR FORCE in the storage register for A$ and all subsequent reference to A$ will use that particular text until A$ is assigned a new value. The value of A$ can be requested through an INPUT or READ statement and may be printed with a PRINT statement.

Returning again to the beam problem, statement 170 tests the maximum deflection of the beam and, if found to be unacceptable, the program jumps to statement 300 to print a warning message. A string input may then be used at this stage to ask the user whether a new value of I should be tried, as in:

```
310 INPUT "DO YOU WANT TO TRY A NEW VALUE OF I" ; A$
320 IF A$="Y" THEN GOTO 150
330 IF A$="N" THEN GOTO 280
340 GOTO 310
```

Line 310 asks for a value (the reply) to be assigned to A$ and lines 320 – 340 compare A$ with 'Y' and if found to be true there is a jump to statement 150 which asks for the value of I; if false, the execution continues to statement 330. Although not absolutely necessary, statement 330 compares A$ with 'N' and jumps to statement 280 if the comparison is true. Otherwise it continues to statement 340 which causes a jump back to statement 310 to repeat the question. The reason for including the second check is that if it is not included, any reply other than 'Y' would be assumed to mean a negative reply, including an inadvertent additional character before or after 'Y'. This demonstrates the point that string comparisons must be exact, even allowing for spaces, for an IF statement to be true. It is therefore evident that this program will only accept 'Y' or 'N' for Yes or No. A response of 'YES' or 'NO' would not be accepted.

There are many other string operations available depending on the particular version of BASIC being used. For example, commands are available to form new strings consisting of parts of existing strings (LEFT$,RIGHT$ and MID$) and a string consisting of numbers may be converted to numeric form using VAL, or a number may be converted to a string by using STR$.

5.15 Program remarks

A listing of a program can often look rather overwhelming and it is helpful to include the programmer's comments at appropriate points to explain what each part of the program is doing. This can be done using the REM or remark statement which, although stored within the program, will be completely ignored by the computer on execution. Several remarks have been included in the beam problem as in:

```
160 REM CHECK MAXIMUM DEFLECTION
```

5.16 Example program

Although many other commands are usually available in most versions of BASIC, almost any design program could be written with the limited statements discussed in this chapter. The beam problem has been used to demonstrate the use of individual statements. These statements can now be combined, and a few similar statements added, to produce a program to calculate and print bending moments and deflections at increments of L/10 along the beam. The results of this program could be used to plot a bending moment diagram and deflection profile and, although the beam example is extremely simple, it would involve relatively few additional statements to include point loads and applied moments using the principle of superposition.

The final program for using a uniformly distributed load is shown in Fig. 5.2. Although input checks and foolproofing procedures (see Chapter 6) have not been included for the sake of clarity, it can be seen that less than half of the statements are used for calculation and program control; the remainder are required for input and output. As programs become more sophisticated the proportion of statements required for calculation and control becomes smaller.

Figure 5.3 shows the data entry and printout of results for an example in which L=5m, E=210 000N/mm^2, W=10kN and I is given initially as:

50 000 000 mm^4 and subsequently as 60 000 000 mm^4.

5.17 Variable arrays

A variable array contains a specified number of 'subscripted variables' or 'elements', with only one variable name. Any one element of the array may be identified uniquely by the use of an array 'subscript'. For example, array X could have 20 elements defined by X(1), X(2) ... X(I) ... X(20) where I is the general subscript. This is known as a 'single dimension' array because it only has one subscript, and it is an array of 20 elements.

Most programming languages use at least a two-dimensional array and many versions of BASIC use three or more. A two-dimensional array could be as shown in Fig. 5.4 in which the general description of any element would be X(I , J), i.e. X (row number, column number). In this particular example the array is of size 10 × 10 and has 100 elements. A three- or more dimensional array is obviously very difficult to show on a two-dimensional sheet of paper.

The benefit of arrays is that hundreds or even thousands of values may all be assigned to one variable name but each value is addressed individually by specifying the subscripts of its location in the array. Although the significance of this may not

```
100 REM PROGRAM TO PRINT MOMENTS AND DEFLECTIONS AT
SPECIFIED
110 REM POINTS ALONG A SIMPLY SUPPORTED BEAM WITH UDL
120 INPUT "ENTER BEAM LENGTH (M)";L
130 INPUT "ENTER TOTAL U.D.L. (KN) ";W
140 INPUT "ENTER MODULUS OF ELASTICITY (N/MM∧2)";E
150 INPUT "ENTER SECOND MOMENT OF AREA (MM∧4)";I
160 REM CHECK MAXIMUM DEFLECTION
170 IF 5*W*L∧3*1E+12/(384*E*I) > L/.36 THEN GOTO 300
180 REM PRINT HEADING
190 PRINT "X", "B.M.", "DEFLECTION"
200 PRINT "(M)", "(KNM)", "(MM)"
210 REM START CALCULATIONS
220 FOR X=0 TO L STEP L/10
230 M=W*X*(L-X)/(2*L)
240 D=W*X*(L∧3-2*L*X∧2+X∧3)*1E12/(24*E*I*L)
250 PRINT X,M,D
260 NEXT X
270 REM END OF CALCULATIONS
280 PRINT "END OF PROGRAM"
290 END
300 PRINT "MAXIMUM DEFLECTION > L/360"
310 INPUT "DO YOU WANT TO TRY A NEW VALUE OF I";A$
320 IF A$="Y" THEN GOTO 150
330 IF A$="N" THEN GOTO 280
340 GOTO 310
```

Fig. 5.2 Example program listing

be immediately apparent, it can be appreciated that if the same operation must be carried out on hundreds of values, then this can be achieved with only a few statements. For example, if an array A contains 50 elements, the value of each element requiring to be transformed to its logarithm, and stored in array B also containing 50 elements, then:

```
100 FOR J = 1 TO 50
110 B(J) = LOG(A(J))
120 NEXT J
```

is all that is needed. Statement 110 simply says that the Jth element of array B is equal to the logarithm of the Jth element of array A.

If the same operation is required for a two-dimensional array C of size 10 × 10 producing array D (10 × 10) then the 'nested' loops:

```
100 FOR J = 1 TO 10
110 FOR K = 1 TO 10
120 D(J,K) = LOG (C(J,K))
130 NEXT K
140 NEXT J
```

would carry out 100 logarithmic transformations in only five program statements.

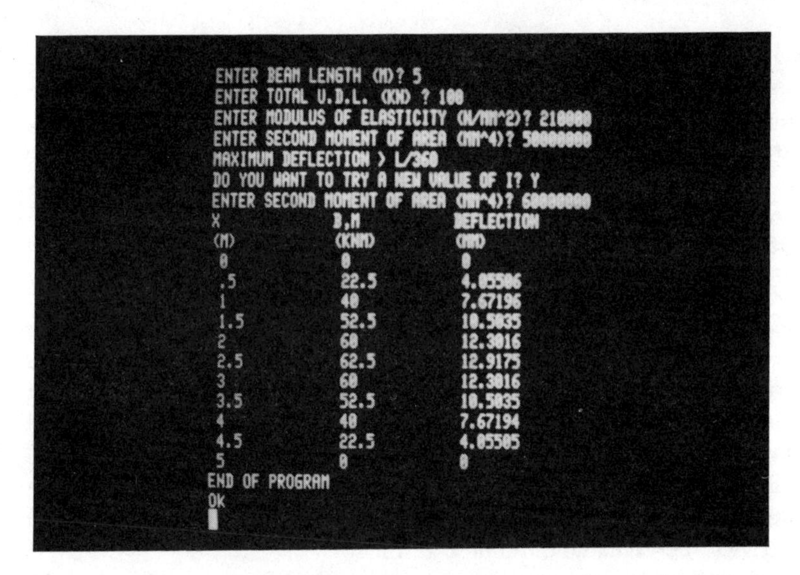

Fig. 5.3 Program displays, user responses and results of example program

	Col. 1	Col. 2		Col. J		Col. 10
Row 1	X(1, 1)	X(1, 2)	...	X(1, J)	...	X(1, 10)
Row 2	X(2, 1)	X(2, 2)	...	X(2, J)	...	X(2, 10)
	...	...	...	...	...	...
	...	...	...	...	...	...
Row I	X(I, 1)	X(I, 2)	...	X(I, J)	...	X(I, 10)
	...	...	...	...	...	...
Row 10	X(10,1)	X(10,2)	...	X(10, J)	...	X(10,10)

Fig. 5.4 A two-dimensional variable array

Although not of immediate relevance to arrays, the operation of nested loops is demonstrated in the above example. The simple rule is that the innermost loop is completed first before incrementing the next. For any value of J, K steps from 1 to 10 before J steps to its next value. This can be visualised as each row of the array in turn being calculated from left to right.

If an array is to be used in a program its name must be specified as an array before the first reference to the name in a program statement. This is done by using the DIM (dimension) statement as in:

```
10 DIM X(10,10)
```

In many versions of BASIC it is not essential to use a DIM statement if the subscript has a maximum value no greater than 10. While this would save a statement, it is good practice always to include a DIM statement to avoid confusion in understanding longer programs.

5.18 Variations of BASIC language

At various points in this chapter we have noted that certain features vary from one version of BASIC to another. Although this will be of little consequence if applications programs are purchased or developed in-house, problems may arise if a program is to be converted from one make of micro to another, each with its own version of BASIC. The reason for the different versions of BASIC is that the more flexible (and therefore more complex) versions require considerably more memory for the BASIC interpreter. Because memory space is at a premium on smaller micros, the language will be limited and less memory demanding. However, all BASIC features described in this chapter will be available on almost all micros.

We shall not attempt to describe the various language differences because of the large number of versions available. However, following our arguments in Chapter 4, there is every reason to try to adopt a standard BASIC language. One such standard is MBASIC, (a tradename of Microsoft Inc.) which is a very powerful, and memory demanding, language available on most micros controlled by the CP/M and MSDOS operating systems. There is a reasonable chance that programs written in MBASIC can be transferred to a wide range of other micros.

In subsequent chapters we shall be using MBASIC to demonstrate our views on good programming practice and to show how disc file systems operate. For those readers with access to a micro with its own version of BASIC, the principles will be the same, but the statements may differ.

Chapter 6

Applications programming

Those unfamiliar with computers may be forgiven for thinking that any two programs which profess to serve the same purpose – for example, a plane frame analysis – will be more or less identical, at least from the user's standpoint if not in the details of the program itself. This in fact is far from being the case, and in this chapter we shall try to highlight those features which represent 'good' software. We shall do this by discussing how to plan and develop microcomputer programs for design and in doing so shall also be suggesting points to look for when assessing commercial software. Before doing this, however, we shall look briefly at certain aspects of writing computer programs, and we can usefully divide these into two, not necessarily distinct, stages. The first of these has traditionally been referred to as systems analysis and the second may be termed detail programming or encoding – i.e. the process of physically writing the program statements.

The process of systems analysis is one in which the problem and its solution are structured in such a way that the subsequent detailed programming can be carried out efficiently, and this will normally involve the following steps:

(a) a clear definition of the problem to be solved;
(b) selection of a suitable method of solution (algorithm);
(c) identification of the required input data and results;
(d) formulation of some type of 'flow chart'.

As can be seen, the process involves little more than translating the defined problem into a series of smaller, more manageable sections. For a simple problem this may be no more than:

DEFINE REQUIRED DATA
CALCULATE ACCORDING TO PRESCRIBED METHOD OF SOLUTION
PRESENT RESULTS

By subdividing the problem in this manner and defining the method of solution, required results and necessary input data, the systems analysis provides a framework within which the program can be written in detail.

The detailed program writing involves translating these procedures into a series of program statements using a high-level language such as BASIC, thus enabling the program to be processed by the computer. A program cannot, however, be considered fully developed even at this stage and it is, of course, necessary to test the program rigorously and to provide detailed documentation describing it, how it should be used, and the range of problems it can accommodate. These aspects of program development have not always received the attention which they ought, and many programs suffer particularly from poor documentation.

In this chapter we shall be concentrating on the systems analysis and discussing both the provision of good documentation and checking procedures. Detailed aspects of program writing are covered more fully in Chapters 5 and 8.

6.1 General program objectives

Apart from performing the required function which will be specific to each application, there are some general objectives which program developers should strive to achieve.

In the case of programs operating on a large machine, a programmer's primary objective should almost certainly be to minimise the execution time of the program, because this is the most important factor in terms of cost in use. This speed may be achieved rather inefficiently, partly at the expense of using additional memory, but on a modern mainframe computer this is usually a marginal disadvantage. More important, however, data input will need to be as efficient as possible, resulting in less 'user-friendly' programs with data being entered via a data file – simply a block of numbers prepared in accordance with the prescribed instructions contained in the manual. Microcomputers, on the other hand, are quite different in that their cost of use is largely independent of execution time, but with relatively limited amounts of usable memory, storage is at a premium. This is an important difference, but even more important is that a microcomputer, being essentially a 'dedicated' facility, is ideally suited to interactive computing. In general, therefore, we should develop microcomputer programs not for the benefit of the CPU but rather for the end user, and a first priority should be that programs are easy to use rather than computationally efficient.

With this overall objective in mind, we can now begin to plan the program, and in doing so shall initially consider certain general points. These include the degree of control which should be provided to the user, the range of problems which the program should be able to treat, and the point in the design process at which the user should initially enter and finally leave the program.

6.1.1 Control

As described in Chapter 2, one of the great attractions of interactive computing is that decisions need not be preprogrammed, but can be made by the user by referring control to him at the appropriate points in the program. The identification of these points in the design process where the user should assume control is therefore very important. Whereas too little control creates some of the problems which have been experienced with batch processing, if the user has to provide too much control the use of the program becomes longwinded and tedious. Perhaps the best guidance is that any decision beyond the control of the designer – e.g. rules relating to Codes of Practice – should be taken automatically within the program, but those requiring some judgement should be made by the user. Even so, in some applications this may result in excessive amounts of data input or decision making, and a useful facility in such circumstances is to provide output indicating data which is being used or decisions which are being taken, and offering the engineer the opportunity of overriding these 'default' values.

The method of expressing control by the user can also be made easier by providing menus – i.e. lists of possible decisions from which the user makes his selection. At an early stage in the program planning we should therefore identify not only those points where decisions should be taken by the user, but also what alternatives he may wish to select.

6.1.2 Flexibility

General purpose programs can be extremely useful, but this is at the expense of the need to provide additional input to define the problem. It is often preferable to have a number of smaller programs, each designed for a specific purpose, and a good example of this is frame analysis. General purpose frame analysis programs require a generalised form of data input with the frame geometry, for instance, defined in terms of co-ordinates and a member connection list. This necessitates not only large quantities of input data, but also a form of input which the user may find difficult to interpret immediately, leading to a much greater risk of data errors. If, on the other hand, the frame type is specified more precisely – e.g. a multi-bay, multi-storey, rectangular framework – frame geometry can be defined simply in terms of bay widths and storey heights. In this way the amount of data required is dramatically reduced and is in a form immediately recognisable by the user. The presentation of results can be similarly simplified.

When deciding on the range of problems which should be accommodated, it is therefore important to avoid the temptation to cover every possible condition. As a first stage the range of examples of a particular type of problem should be identified. In many cases a significant majority of these will fall within a much more limited range – for instance, a firm dealing with the design of steel portal frames may find that although the range of structures includes multi-bay, asymmetric and propped portals, 90 per cent of cases are simple symmetric single bay frames. A program written for this specific case is therefore likely to be of greater value than a more general one which, although capable of dealing with the full range of problems, would be more difficult to use for the great majority of cases. It may be that a number of programs (some of which may contain many identical routines) are required to effectively cover the range of problems which occur frequently, but this should not be seen as a disadvantage.

6.1.3 Comprehensiveness

In the same way that it is necessary to identify the flexibility of the program, so the point at which the designer first enters and finally leaves the program should be carefully considered. Programs which carry out comprehensive calculations for large engineering schemes and by implication require large amounts of input data may be less attractive in terms of ease of use than relatively small programs capable of dealing with just a small part of the overall design. A reinforced concrete frame building, for example, is normally designed as a series of components – slabs, beams, columns and foundations – with loadings determined at each stage being carried forward to the next. Whilst it would be possible to incorporate the routines dealing with the design and associated analysis for all these elements within one program, the limited memory capacity of microcomputers would make this rather inappropriate. In any case, the advantages to be gained are marginal, and a series of smaller programs dealing with slab design, subframe analysis, moment redistribution, beam, column and foundation design would be much more suitable, reflecting as it does the way in which a designer would currently approach the problem. Furthermore, because it is only a very limited amount of data which is to be transferred from one stage to the next, this system of small programs can often be written in such a way that data from the preceding section can be automatically accessed at subsequent stages from disc files.

6.2 Optimising design routines

As mentioned in section 2.4.2, one of the areas in which computers have traditionally enjoyed some success is in fully automated design applications, the most common being the design of steel portal frames, in which the 'optimum' design is determined by the computer. This facility for converging on the best solution is seen by some as a major advantage of using computers but, whilst this may be so in other engineering disciplines where production costs can be more readily identified and design costs may be offset against the production in large numbers, it is less obviously worthwhile in most civil engineering applications. This is because of the type of criteria generally used in the selection of the optimum solution, the most common being minimum quantity of material. In practice, other factors such as construction costs and details, and material availability may be even more important. It would be inappropriate or extremely complex to include these in any optimising routine, yet their omission must detract from the validity of the optimisation. Indeed, these are exactly the sort of loosely defined considerations which are much more effectively dealt with by the human than by the computer as discussed in section 2.2.

One advantage of optimising is that it overcomes the inherent drawbacks of batch processing because the problem is totally pre-defined and automatic. This, however, is something which is negated by the very nature of the microcomputer. Furthermore, programs incorporating optimising routines are often large and, even if it were possible to mount them on a micro, they would probably be very slow to execute. Optimisation would therefore seem to offer little advantage in civil engineering design programs for microcomputers. Moreover, there are disadvantages of such techniques, notably that the engineer is reduced to little more than a data processor, with little responsibility other than selecting the program and entering the data. This rightly raises fears within the profession that there might develop a generation of young engineers with no intuition for engineering solutions; or even worse that such engineers could be replaced by unqualified computer operators. A better approach is to allow the user to explore alternatives and make the necessary judgements to converge on a preferred solution. Not only does this avoid the problems referred to but also a facility is provided whereby young engineers can readily gain substantial 'experience' of possible solutions. By enabling easy modification of individual items of data, an inexperienced engineer can rapidly explore the sensitivity of a design to various parameters in a way which would not be economically possible using manual methods.

Microcomputers, therefore, do not require automated optimising design programs, nor are they in general suitable for such application. In any case, the disadvantages of optimisation are often much greater than any possible advantages, and we would therefore conclude that such procedures are generally inappropriate for interactive design programs on a micro.

6.3 External program structure

Because interactive programs have as a primary objective good communication between the computer and the user it is appropriate to examine what might be referred to as the external structure of the program, that is, how the elements of the program appear to be interconnected from the user's viewpoint.

A program operating on a batch process system will typically consist of three distinct sections – input of data, calculation, and output of results. These are arranged sequentially and may even be contained within three separate but linked programs each performing one of the functions listed. In whatever way it is arranged, the program will operate independently of the user, except, of course, it is he who will supply the data and he who will interpret the results. The external structure of a batch-processing program could therefore be described simply as enter data – interpret results.

Interactive programs are similar in that data input, calculation and output are all constituent parts of the program, but an additional control function is also included. The importance of this in allowing control to remain with the user and its implications in terms of computer-aided design were discussed in Chapter 2, and it is clear that, where appropriate, full advantage should be taken of this facility to make the best use of an interactive computing facility. We have already mentioned that interactive programs should be written for the benefit of the user and, if we are also to incorporate this control stage, our programs are going to appear quite different from conventional batch-processing programs.

We now have four different functions which must be included, namely enter data, calculation, output results, and control. The whole program can then be considered as a series of such blocks, each containing some or all of these functions. The length of each block will depend essentially upon how much data input or calculation is required before intermediate results are displayed and the user is given the opportunity of making a decision. This will vary not only from application to application, but also from one part of the program to another. Once the extent of the calculation within any block has been decided, the required data, the form in which the results will be displayed and the alternative decisions which the user may wish to make can then be considered. In this way the external structure of an interactive program will appear as a series of input data, display results, decision sequences.

6.3.1 Screen displays

Since communication between the computer and the user is essentially through the VDU, the way in which the screen displays are arranged is very important. In general, as information is shown on the screen, (which, as described in Chapter 3, can typically display 24 lines of text 80 characters wide) the text 'scrolls up' with the newest information shown at the bottom of the screen, all preceding lines moving up by one line and the top (oldest) line simply rolling off the top of the screen. This is equivalent to reading a manuscript on a scroll, and, whilst this may be quite adequate, it can give a rather untidy presentation. A better scheme is to treat the display as a series of 'pages' – once one page is full the screen is cleared and additional information is displayed. This is particularly appropriate where we are considering different functions such as data input or displaying results as each of these can be accommodated on a clean page with an appropriate title, enabling the user to interpret the text more clearly. Therefore, in planning a program we can think in terms of such pages, and in doing so we are already beginning to give more consideration to the user than we might in planning a program for batch processing.

It will be apparent that there are basically three types of conversation which the user may have with the computer, which are as follows:

(a) Data input, in which the user is 'talking' to the computer;
(b) Information display, in which the machine is 'talking' to the user;
(c) Control, in which the machine asks which of a series of specified alternative courses of action the user wishes to select, and he responds accordingly.

Depending on how it is arranged, data checking may be a cross between data input and information display, or may be incorporated as part of the data input.

These in essence describe all of the types of conversation which the user and the machine may have using an interactive program, and it is useful to think in terms of each of these as a typical screen display (i.e. a transcription of that conversation). By arranging appropriate screen displays in the required sequence we will be able to further develop the idea of program structure.

This can be illustrated by using the simple example of a program dealing with the design of a steel beam. The way in which this would normally be done is represented in the flow chart shown in Fig. 2.2. This could be expressed in a little more detail in terms of screen displays as shown in Fig. 6.1. In this way the designer is able to provide a fairly precise framework within which the program can be developed.

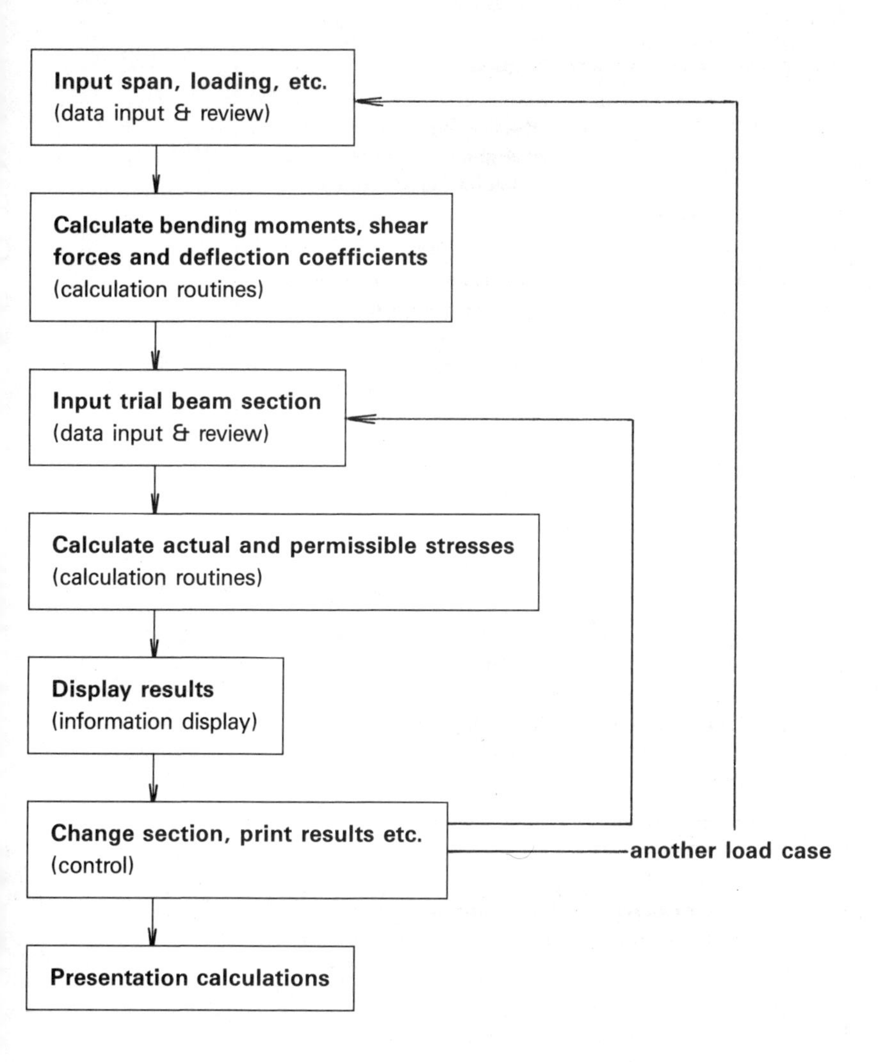

Fig. 6.1 The design sequence for a steel beam expressed as series of screen 'pages'

6.3.2 Flow charts

If an experienced designer were asked to describe in note form the general procedure which he followed for a particular type of problem, he would probably be able to do this quite clearly and simply. Furthermore, expressing this in terms of the typical screen displays described above should present no additional difficulties. This is in

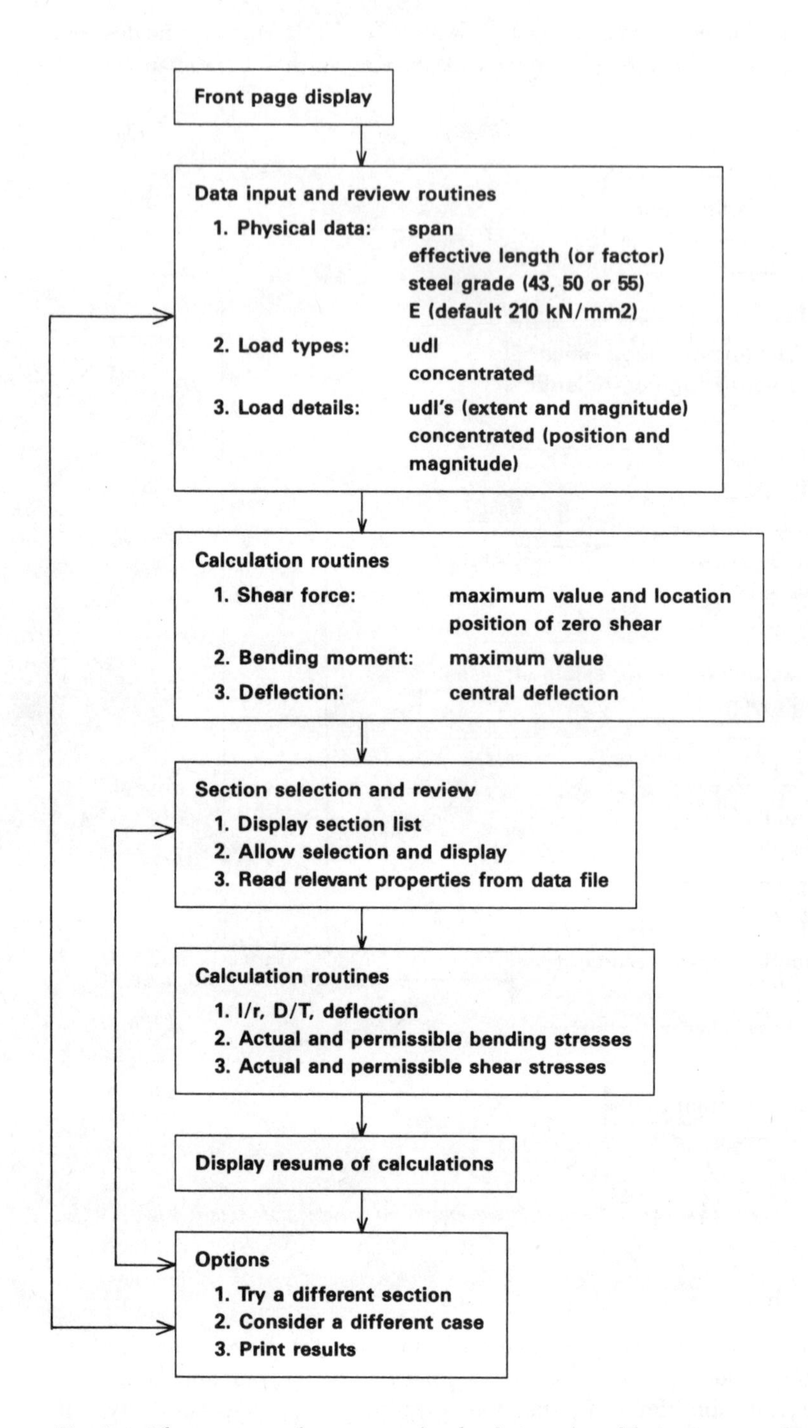

Fig. 6.2 The structure of a program for the design of steel beams expressed as a flow chart

essence a form of flow chart – not in the conventional sense of the word meaning a diagrammatic representation of the internal operations and paths through the program, but rather a description of how the program should run from the viewpoint of the user. In essence the sequence of screen displays indicated in Fig. 6.1 could be extended and a flow chart developed as shown in Fig. 6.2.

6.4 More detailed considerations

Having divided the program into a series of pages and established a structure in the form of a flow chart, it is then necessary to decide in detail how each corresponding section of the program should be arranged, and we can look at each of the page types in turn.

6.4.1 Data input

As we have already discussed, computers can relieve the engineer of a great deal of tedious work, and this is one of the most important advantages of computer-aided design. However, this will not be realised if the computer (i.e. the computer program) is itself laborious to use. If this is so, we are simply replacing one mundane method with another and clearly there is no benefit in that.

Computers do require some effort on the part of the user – data must be entered, results must be interpreted, and decisions must be made on the basis of those results. Generally the major effort is in entering the data and, because we need to define the problem precisely, this can be quite significant, depending on the nature of both the problem and the program. We should therefore endeavour to simplify and minimise this task as far as possible, and this can be done in a number of ways.

(a) Hierarchy of input data

Rather than entering all initial data on a single page (which may not in fact be big enough to accommodate it) it is useful to ascribe a hierarchy to individual items and to group items of the same hierarchy on the same page. In the design of a reinforced concrete beam for instance, the span, support conditions and loading will often be predetermined and would occupy the highest priority. This would be entered on the first page of data input. Material properties for concrete and reinforcement may occupy a lower level, as would the beam dimensions, and these might therefore be entered on subsequent page(s). Each page should be given a clear description of the function of that page – e.g. DATA INPUT – CROSS SECTIONAL DETAILS OF BEAM – thus keeping the user clearly informed of the current stage within the program.

Apart from separating data input into sensible groups, such a system enables data to be modified more easily. For instance, if a selected beam section is found to be unsuitable it is only necessary to return to that particular page, whereas if the span or loading were to be modified it is likely that the beam section too would need to be changed. By returning to the appropriate page not only can data at that level of hierarchy be amended but data with lower priorities can also be modified.

(b) Form of data

Clearly, the detailed data requirements of any program will depend upon its purpose, but in general the program should be arranged to accept data in the most convenient and meaningful form to the user. A good example of this is the case of plane frame analysis which requires beam and column stiffnesses in order to complete the solution. These are traditionally entered directly as second moments of area and cross-sectional areas, but, whilst this might be acceptable for a steel frame, it is rather inconvenient for a reinforced concrete frame. In this case it is easier to specify the actual dimensions of the section, and to determine the appropriate stiffnesses within the computer.

In some cases, arranging data in such a form may in fact result in slightly more items to be entered, but this is outweighed by the advantages to the user of less preliminary work, easier checking and editing of the data, and a process which is considerably less prone to errors.

(c) Checks on data for sense and consistency

Because the effort associated with data input may be considerable, it is important that abortive runs should be avoided. Almost all programs contain mathematical expressions which under certain circumstances could result in an error – a common one is trying to divide by zero – and this may happen if inappropriate data is specified, whether by accident or design.

More important, it is possible to make a silly mistake in input, and if this is not noticed, incorrect results will be obtained. The need for positive data checking will be discussed later, but it is clearly useful to trap any items which are obviously erroneous as they are entered. A simple example might be specifying a load on a beam at some point beyond its extremities. Checking such items not only enables the error to be pointed out to the user, but also enables immediate correction.

Some examples of this type of error may in fact be intentional, and it would indeed be frustrating if the user found that he was prevented from using particular data, however improbable, by such an inflexible trapping system. This however can easily be overcome by displaying a warning message if an unusual, but not invalid, value is input. An example might be the use of non-standard concrete strength in reinforced concrete design.

(d) Data prompts

As mentioned in Chapter 5, data can be requested by a program by simply using the INPUT statement with a prompt such as:

```
10 INPUT "WIDTH OF BEAM (mm)";B
```

By including details such as the dimensions to be used the request should become clear and the user should be able to provide the required data correctly and confidently.

Prompts for input data should therefore be clear and unambiguous. In addition they should be concise (without being so brief that they again become open to misinterpretation) and 'friendly' or 'conversational' in style. This simply makes the program a little more pleasant to use which should result in fewer errors and a greater willingness on the part of the designer to use the program.

6.4.2 Data checking

Because it is very easy to make a mistake when entering data it is necessary to provide a means of verifying that the information provided is correct. Without such a facility, incorrect data could go unnoticed, and the results obtained would be 'wrong'. Similarly, if the user were to realise that a mistake had been made it might be difficult to make the necessary corrections without starting again from the beginning. Clearly, both circumstances must be avoided, which can be done by providing a data-checking facility which requires positive confirmation by the user that the data specified is correct. This can be accomplished in a number of different ways.

(a) Checking of individual items

A very simple way of providing this data check would be to display each value immediately after it has been entered and to request confirmation that it is correct. If the user gives this confirmation, the next item is requested and displayed for verification and so on. Items identified as incorrect result in the request for that item being repeated, followed by an opportunity to check the revised value.

Whilst this method means that mistakes can be rectified immediately, and that the only additional input effort required if data has been specified incorrectly is the revised value of that particular item, it does require confirmation of every piece of data individually. Not only is this a tedious process but it may also make it more difficult to detect errors.

(b) Checking of complete data

A better approach would be to check all data input at any particular stage. This would certainly be less tedious and make errors more apparent, but if mistakes are found it would be necessary to enter all the data (including correct items) again. Not only is this time-consuming and tedious but it also introduces the real possibility of making additional errors. A more sensible scheme might be to check blocks of data corresponding to the various input pages. However, this would still mean a considerable amount of input effort if just one item needed correcting.

(c) Data check menus

A method which combines the ease of checking blocks of data with the ease of correcting individual items is to use a menu system. It is again convenient to think in terms of data input pages and corresponding displays for reviewing or checking each block of data. These displays should give each item a unique reference number which the user can specify if he wishes to amend its value. In this way data can be checked in blocks but corrected individually to provide a very efficient method of verification. An example of this is shown in Fig. 6.3.

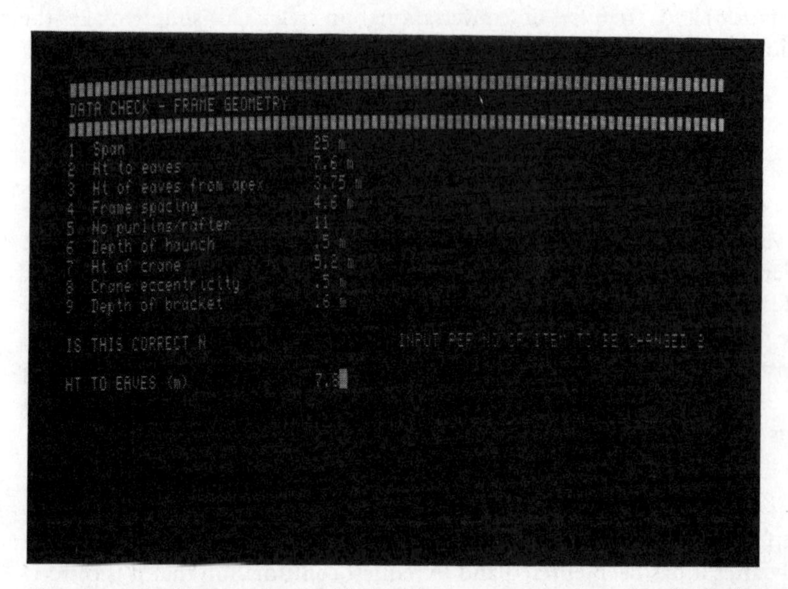

Fig. 6.3 Checking of data in blocks allows easy correction of individual items

In presenting this facility for reviewing data, the screen display should be clear, concise and unambiguous, and it should of course be arranged to make the checking as easy as possible. In some cases it may be preferable to display the information in a different form from that in which the data was originally entered. One way of doing this is to make use of graphical display where appropriate. The geometry of a plane frame, for example, is most efficiently checked by displaying on the screen a diagram of the frame defined by the input data. This not only provides a clear indication of any input errors, but also checks that the program has correctly interpreted the data. Another example is where items are specified by reference number, defining data within the program or perhaps contained within a disc file. In these circumstances it is preferable to display some details of the information as retrieved rather than the reference number itself. This provides not only information which is more easily assimilated but also confirms that the computer has interpreted the user's instructions as intended. An example of this is shown in Fig. 6.4 in which steel beam sections have been specified by a reference number, but the data check is effected through a display of the corresponding serial size. Note that the advantage of using this form of data input is that one item can be used to identify a larger quantity of data (in this case cross-sectional dimensions and properties) contained within the program or in a data file, thereby considerably reducing input effort.

6.4.3 Information display

As the name implies, this type of display simply provides the user with particular information at various stages throughout a run. It may, for instance, display results which will form the basis for a subsequent decision to be made by the user, such as:

MAXIMUM BM = 492.1 kNm

press RETURN to continue

Note that the second line simply allows the user to contemplate the results for as long as he wishes before proceeding to a subsequent part of the program.

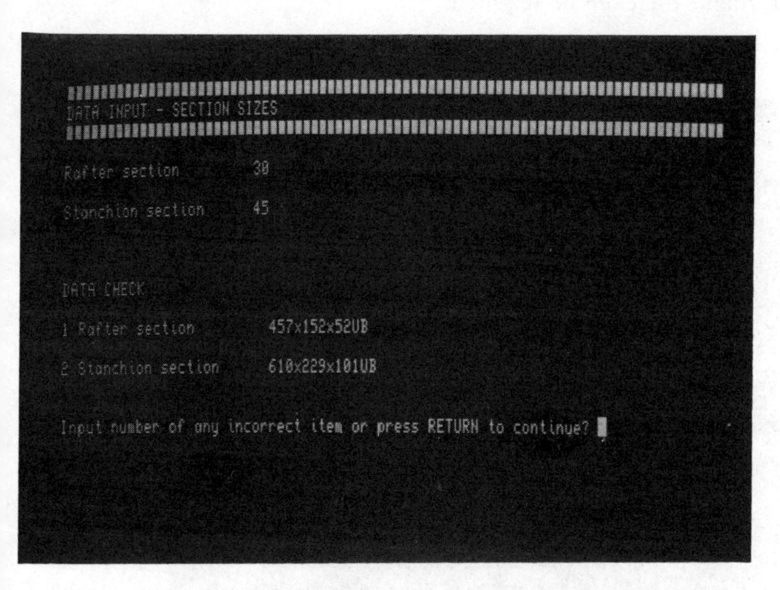

Fig. 6.4 Data such as serial sizes for rolled steel sections is most efficiently input by coded reference number; data checks must, however, include full details

Another example of this type of page includes providing explanatory information, such as:

DATA IS BEING READ FROM FILE

which may do no more than reassure the user that he has not been forgotten, and may also serve as a means of helping him follow the current working of the program.

6.4.4 Control

The pages which allow the user to exert control over the program are most important in providing the interactive facility which is so valuable in computer-aided design. They enable the user to dictate the next sequence of operations, to decide whether the design is sufficiently refined, whether modifications should be made to the data and so on. The possible selections at any stage can be presented in the form of an option list or menu similar to those used for data checking. An example is shown in Fig. 6.5, and by entering the appropriate number the user may select the desired course of action.

Clearly, the options which are provided will depend upon the type of problem which the program is capable of solving and the particular stage within the program at which the options are provided. Most designs involve some degree of trial-and-error and require separate modes of behaviour to be treated (a reinforced concrete beam for instance must be designed for flexure, shear and deflection). Options to review data, or proceed to a further set of calculations, as well as print the results or save data, might therefore be required.

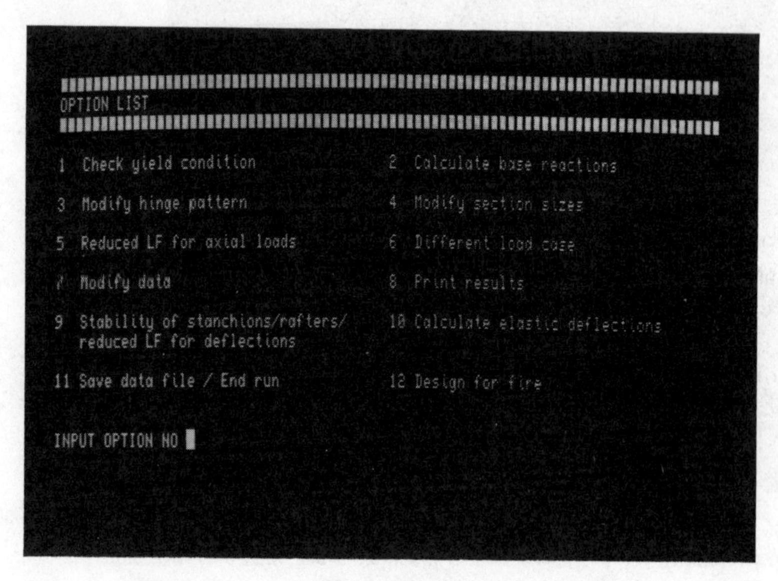

Fig. 6.5 Option lists or menus provide an efficient means by which the user may exercise control over the program execution

6.4.5 Executive parts of program (calculating routines)

We have looked at the planning of an interactive computer program and studied in some detail how this should be organised to the greatest benefit of the user. One important aspect which we have not covered, however, is planning the executive parts of the program – i.e. those sections in which the calculations are actually performed. In some respects, this is the most important part of the program in that it performs the essential function and must therefore be 'correct' in both mathematical and engineering terms. Exactly how the calculations are performed is, however, relatively unimportant. The user should be familiar with the method and assumptions on which the program is based, but, as he has no direct conversation with this part of the program, the exact representation of the theory in a high-level computer language is of little concern to him. For instance, somebody who has always used moment-distribution for manual solution should not be concerned that the program he is using employs matrix methods. Nevertheless, it is essential that the user is familiar with the principles on which the program is based, for what problems it is valid, and so on, and in this respect documentation is very important. This will be discussed later in section 6.8.

Therefore the selection of an appropriate algorithm – i.e. specific method of solution – is relatively unimportant to the user, as long as it will provide sufficient accuracy and cope with the required range of problems. In making his selection the program writer should think in terms of the amount of memory required, including the size of arrays, number of variables and the length of the program itself. This aspect is particularly important on micros in which available memory is relatively small.

The programmer may also wish to consider speed of processing when selecting an algorithm; a faster program is in general preferable to a slow one. However, it is important to maintain perspective in terms of speed. Whereas mainframe charges are largely based on CPU time used, the cost of using a microcomputer is virtually independent of such. The cost implications of a 'slow' program are therefore not associated directly with computing costs, but with the cost of the professional engineer's time waiting for the results, and savings of even a few seconds (a long time in computing terms!) are of little consequence. Bearing in mind that microcomputers are usually immediately accessible and should be easy to use, the problem of processing time is seldom an important factor. This means that methods currently used on large machines may not always be the ideal ones to use on a microcomputer, and that considerations of required memory and indeed ease of programming and usage may be more important than speed. Algorithms should be selected with this in mind.

6.4.6 Design data

We have suggested that the methods adopted for design using a microcomputer should as far as possible follow those currently used for manual calculation. This not only facilitates the checking of results, but also provides the user with a greater awareness and understanding of the working of the program. Unfortunately, not all manual methods are ideally suited to computer application. This is not necessarily because the method is inefficient in terms of computing time, which we have already seen is not an overriding factor; it is rather that some methods are not capable of being expressed easily in explicit mathematical and logical relationships. Because civil engineering design and analysis has traditionally been carried out by hand, the rules which govern it are generally presented for ease of use by an engineer with a calculator. We thus have an abundance of design charts and tables, all intended to make life easier for the manual designer, and with little thought given to computer application. Faced with such a situation the program developer has a number of alternatives – to store the tabulated information as discrete items of data, to use a 'curve fitting' procedure in order to obtain an empirical design relationship, or to work from basic principles. A fourth alternative is to require the engineer to interpret the charts or curves manually and to provide specific data for the particular problem at the appropriate points during the run.

(a) Data bank

Providing standard data – either within the program or on a separate data file – does enable tabulated information to be available in exactly the same way as it is to the manual designer. An added bonus is that where interpolation between values is permitted, this can be easily and automatically included within the program. The main disadvantage of such an approach is that it can consume considerable amounts of memory, and on a microcomputer with relatively small storage capacity this can prove difficult. Nevertheless, for small tables and simple applications, such an approach is quite valid and is easy, if somewhat tedious, to program. Using this method the accuracy obtained will of course be exactly the same as if the tables were used by hand.

(b) Curve fitting

It is a relatively straightforward procedure to derive a mathematical expression which is a 'good fit' to a particular curve. Any design curve could therefore be treated in this way and effectively be reproduced within the computer. This is in fact a more condensed way of storing a relationship between two or more variables than providing a data bank, and does therefore have attractions for use on a microcomputer. However, where design curves are used in civil and structural engineering they are often presented in large numbers, and include several variables. To establish mathematical expressions for such curves is generally possible but a different expression would probably be required for each curve. This would again create problems of storage. Moreover, because of the likely complexity of such expressions, it would be tedious (if not difficult) to program and prone to error. Curve fitting is inevitably an approximation to the actual relationship, although, depending on the level of sophistication used, it should be possible to obtain sufficiently accurate relationships.

(c) Basic theory

A more satisfactory way of presenting the design relationships is to resort to the principles on which the tables and curves are themselves based. This is often the most efficient way of including such information within a program in terms of storage requirements and, purely from a technical point of view, is the most attractive since it should provide (if anything) a more accurate relationship than the published curves or tables. Unfortunately, the theory on which such information is based is not always readily available, although there is an increasing tendency to follow the American practice of publishing formulae or algorithms as well as tables or curves in Codes of Practice and design manuals. Such a development is to be welcomed but there are still a number of areas where the source of design relationships is obscure or simply not stated.

(d) Manual interpretation of design charts and tables

Using an interactive computer program it is of course possible to avoid this problem altogether. At any point in the calculations where information from a table or curve is required, the user could be provided with sufficient data to enable him to determine the appropriate value and enter this in the same way as any other item. Calculations could then proceed in the normal way until further information of this form was needed and so on. Such a method is not without its attractions – the program can remain compact and simple, and the user may feel a greater sense of control over the design. However, such a feeling would clearly be mistaken – control is going from the computer to the design chart, not to the user; he is simply acting as the interpreter between machine and chart. Furthermore, such a procedure would soon become tiresome, and it does not represent the most efficient use of either man or machine. If available memory is limited, a better approach might be to provide the appropriate data on a disc file as described in section 7.2.

6.5 Printed output

We have argued that the screen displays and the interactive conversations correspond to the engineer's rough working. Similarly, the printed output should correspond to the presentation calculations, providing a permanent record of the calculations for the purposes of checking, preparation of drawings and validation. It is often preferable, therefore, to allow these results to be printed at the end of the run, and without further interaction from the user, since they represent no more than a formal record of his final design selection.

The production of presentation calculations in this way is a bonus since it need involve none of the engineer's time, and it is important that the form of the printed output is suitable for its intended use. This will mean that it will be quite different from the screen displays where the user is interested essentially in the results, rather than the details of the calculations, but where a number of alternatives selected by him will have been successively displayed. Clearly, only the final selection is required for the printed copy, but this should be in sufficient detail to enable a check using conventional methods. This latter point is most important since it overcomes to a large extent the concern which many feel about responsibility for the final design. This point is discussed more fully in section 10.5.

Like the screen displays, the printed output should be paged, the format being the same as for traditional manual calculations. All input data should of course be printed, with the detailed form of the calculations depending upon the particular application. The use of some diagrammatic representation using a pseudo graphics print-out (available on many dot matrix printers) can be very helpful, as can additional explanatory text, referring, for example, to clauses in the appropriate Codes of Practice. A typical page of printed output is shown in Fig. 6.6.

6.6 Graphics

We have made occasional reference to graphics and suggested that it is of some benefit for some applications. However, it is essential for very few, and, because of the cost and the limitations described in section 3.6, the use of graphics is likely to be less widespread than the more general use of micros in computer-aided design. Nevertheless, such a facility can be very useful and a good compromise is to develop

```
===============================================================================
BROWN SMITH & JONES                             CAVITY WALL DESIGN EXAMPLE
Brunel Mansions                                 TABLE 9 CASE H
Brunel Avenue                                   CW9H
LONDON SW1                                      PAGE 001 OF 002
===============================================================================
DESIGN OF LATERALLY LOADED PANELS     PROGRAM:LLP VERS 1.1 C.Eng Software Group
BS 5628(amended September 1980)       Data stored on file: CW9HTEMP
===============================================================================
REF.       CALCULATIONS             LEAF 1                    LEAF 2
-------------------------------------------------------------------------------

LEGEND:                   ////////////////////    ////////////////////
------ Denotes Free Edge    X                  X   X                  X
///// Denotes Simple Support X                  X   X                  X
XXXXX Denotes Cont. Support X                  X   X                  X
                            X                  X   X                  X
                            X                  X   X                  X
                            X                  X   X                  X
                            XXXXXXXXXXXXXXXXXXXX   XXXXXXXXXXXXXXXXXXXX
          MATERIALS AND CONSTRUCTION
          --------------------------
Figure 2  CAVITY WALL
Table 1   MORTAR DESIGNATION (iii)                 (iii)
Table 3   UNIT              CLAY BRICKS(W.A.7-12%) CONCRETE BLOCKS 2.8N/mm2
          FKXPAR                0.40 N/mm2            0.25 N/mm2
          FKXPERP               1.10 N/mm2            0.40 N/mm2
Figure 2  LEAF THICKNESS         103 mm                100 mm
Table 9   PANEL HEIGHT         2.550 m               2.550 m
          PANEL LENGTH         4.300 m               4.300 m
-------------------------------------------------------------------------------
          PARTIAL SAFETY FACTORS
          ----------------------
Table 4   MATERIAL STRENGTH     3.50
Clause 22 WIND LOAD             1.40
          APPLIED/S.W. LOAD     0.90
-------------------------------------------------------------------------------
          LOADINGS
          --------
          CHARACTERISTIC:
          APPLIED LOAD          2.59 kN/m              1.25 kN/m
          DENSITY               2137 kg/m3             1060 kg/m3
          WIND LOAD             0.80 kN/m2

          DESIGN:
          APPLIED LOAD          2.33 kN/m              1.13 kN/m
          SELF WEIGHT STRESS   0.019 N/mm2/m ht       0.009 N/mm2/m ht
          WIND LOAD             1.12 kN/m2
-------------------------------------------------------------------------------
```

Fig. 6.6 Printed output should be in sufficient detail to enable traditional checking to be carried out (courtesy of Civil Engineering Software Group, Sheffield)

```
==========================================================================
BROWN SMITH & JONES                     CAVITY WALL DESIGN EXAMPLE
Brunel Mansions                         TABLE 9 CASE H
Brunel Avenue                           CW9H
LONDON SW1                              PAGE 002 OF 002
==========================================================================
DESIGN OF LATERALLY LOADED PANELS     PROGRAM:LLP VERS 1.1 C.Eng Software Group
BS 5628(amended September 1980)       Data stored on file: CW9HTEMP
==========================================================================
REF.       CALCULATIONS             LEAF 1                   LEAF 2
--------------------------------------------------------------------------

           DERIVED VALUES
           --------------
Figure 2   EFF. THICKNESS            135 mm
Cl. 36.3   DIMENSIONS            LIMITS b)1 O.K.          LIMITS b)1 O.K.
           ASPECT RATIO             0.593
Table 9    EDGE CONDITIONS            H                        H
           ORTHO. RATIO             0.512                    0.828

Cl.36.4.2  BM COEFF.PAR SPAN        0.010                    0.009
           BM COEFF.PAR EDGE        0.010                    0.009
           BM COEFF.PERP SPAN       0.020                    0.023
           BM COEFF.PERP EDGE       0.020                    0.023
--------------------------------------------------------------------------

           CALCULATED VALUES
           -----------------
           SECTION MODULUS:
           Z PAR SPAN                1768 cm3                 1667 cm3
           Z PAR EDGE                1768 cm3                 1667 cm3
           Z PERP SPAN               1768 cm3                 1667 cm3
           Z PERP EDGE               1768 cm3                 1667 cm3

Cl.36.4.5  MOMENTS OF RESISTANCE:
           PARALLEL SPAN            0.285 kN.m               0.158 kN.m
           PARALLEL EDGE            0.285 kN.m               0.158 kN.m
           PERPEND. SPAN            0.556 kN.m               0.190 kN.m
           PERPEND. EDGE            0.556 kN.m               0.190 kN.m

           DESIGN MOMENTS:
           PARALLEL SPAN            0.133 kN.m               0.094 kN.m
           PARALLEL EDGE            0.133 kN.m               0.094 kN.m
           PERPEND. SPAN            0.261 kN.m               0.113 kN.m
           PERPEND. EDGE            0.261 kN.m               0.113 kN.m

==========================================================================
```

Fig. 6.6 continued

programs which, as an option, can provide a graphics display. This is most easily arranged by creating a data file which can be read from a separate graphics program to produce the necessary screen display. In this way the problems of machine dependency are largely avoided and the program may be operated by a user who does not wish to make the necessary additional investment to provide a graphics facility. Typical examples where the use of graphics is particularly advantageous are in checking data for frame analysis, and displaying bending moment diagrams. These are shown in Figs. 6.7 and 6.8.

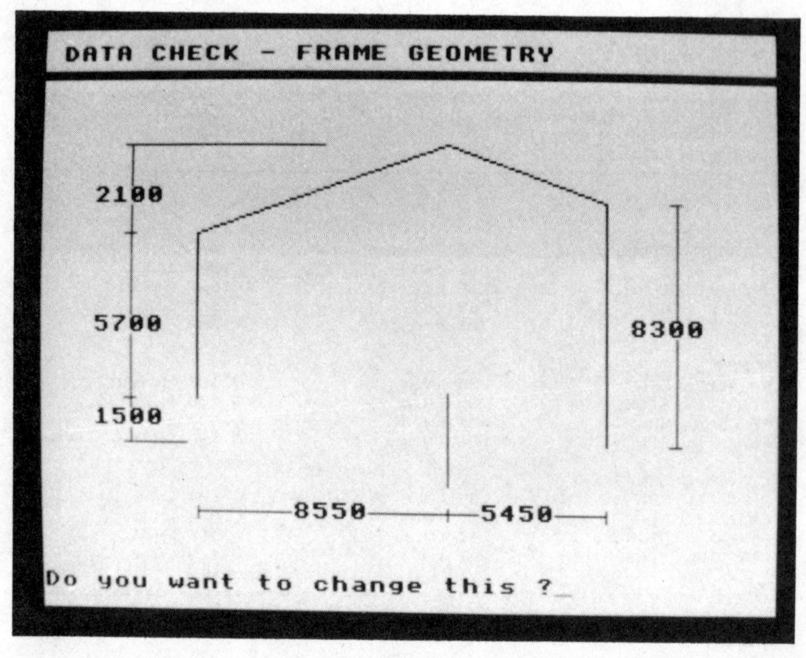

Fig. 6.7 High resolution graphics display, providing an appropriate means of checking frame geometry

6.7 Validation

It is essential that any program is thoroughly checked before it is used in a real design situation. There are a number of aspects which need to be considered in this context and these are discussed in the following sections.

6.7.1 Syntax

With interpreted programs it is possible for a statement to contain a syntax error – that is, a violation of the strict rules of 'grammar' enforced by the high-level language. A typical example is the statement:

```
100 A=0.5(B+C)
```

which should read:

```
100 A=0.5*(B+C)
```

and such an error may not necessarily result in the program failing to run. This is because the particular line will only be interpreted when required, and in large complex programs it is possible that some sections of the program are seldom accessed. The easiest way to carry out a simple check on the syntax is therefore to compile the program, although not all interpreting BASICs support a compiler. This is discussed in more detail in section 4.2.

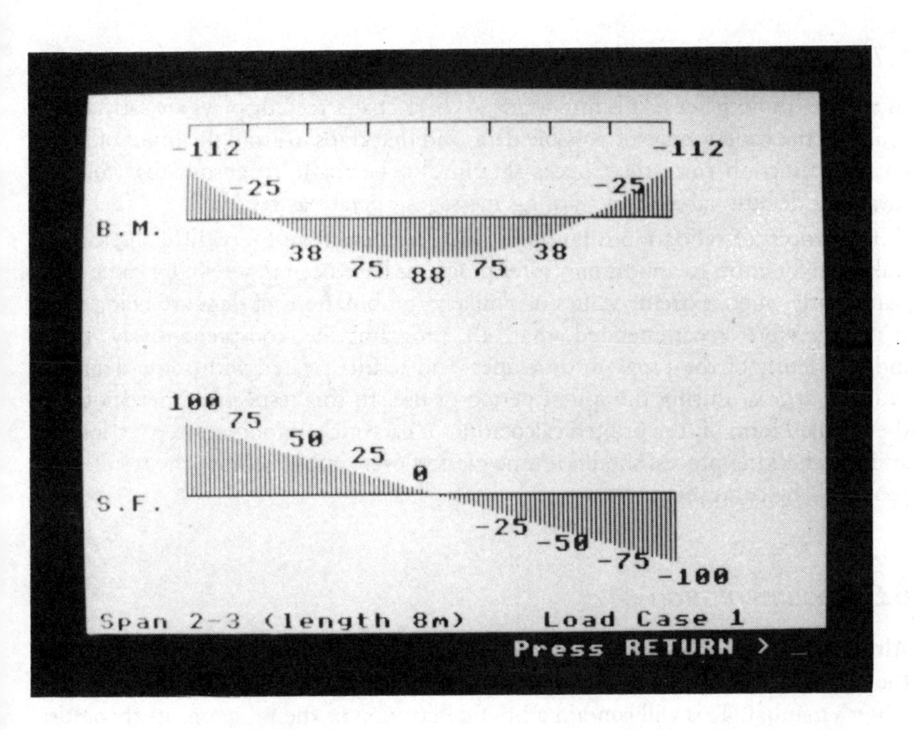

Fig. 6.8 Bending moment diagrams illustrate how high resolution graphics displays can be used to facilitate the interpretation of results (courtesy of I. W. Burgess)

Even a compilation of the program may not detect certain types of error. For instance, a RETURN statement without a GOSUB may not be identified and it is therefore necessary to run the program to provide a more thorough check of this type, attempting in the process to enter every part of the program and access every statement.

6.7.2 Accuracy

It is clearly most important that the program should produce the correct results, and there is no real substitute for running as many examples as possible and comparing the results with those obtained either manually or from other sources. Firms which have a stockpile of design records have an ideal source of such data. It is also useful to check that the program responds sensibly to small changes in data, and where possible, the same answer is obtained when the same problem is defined in different ways.

With interactive computing where there may be a very large number of possible combinations of routes through the program it is difficult to be sure that every path has been checked. Nevertheless, the validation should attempt to cover the whole range of input data, and follow as many routes as possible through the program.

6.7.3 Formatting, error trapping, etc.

In a more cosmetic sense it is important to check that screen displays are satisfactory, again for the widest range of possible data, and that traps to avoid the input of illegal data all function correctly. Checks should also be made to ensure that routines involving default values and warning messages operate as required.

The process of validation is both extremely important and very difficult. It is not unknown for errors to appear only after programs have been in service for some time, particularly where extreme values or unlikely combinations of data are being used. It is therefore recommended that all programs be comprehensively tested independently of the program developer, and results treated with some degree of caution, at least during the initial period of use. In this respect the need for, and the detailed form of, the printed calculations is extremely important (see section 6.5) and the checking process should not be glossed over simply because the results were produced by computer.

6.8 Documentation

Although the program should be largely self-contained with prompts for data and the displays of results being unambiguous, all programs should be accompanied by a user's manual. This will contain a brief description of the program, its theoretical basis, its capabilities and limitations, the input data required, any standard values assumed within the program, and the form of the output. Some of this information could also be usefully incorporated in screen displays at the appropriate points during the program run, or as help overlays as described in section 8.4.

A useful way of presenting this information about how to use an interactive program is to provide an example of the sequence of possible screen displays with footnotes explaining the nature of the display. In this way the user can be 'talked through' a typical run in full detail; there should be no screen display which is not described in this way.

It may also be useful to provide standard data sheets for both input and output so that the user comes to the computer prepared with data in a suitable form, and can readily note appropriate results.

Too often the documentation is an afterthought and is carelessly prepared. The manual should be easy to read, and both clear and concise in its instructions. It is frequently the first point of contact a user has with the program and is therefore of considerable importance.

6.9 Types of problem suitable for computer-aided design

We discussed in Chapter 2 the nature of design and how this related to computer-aided design techniques using either batch or interactive processing. The broad conclusion that interactive computing now provides an effective means of treating any design process will now be considered in greater detail. Certainly interactive CAD does have enormous potential in civil engineering because such design inevitably involves calculations and formal procedures. However, we should also give some attention to considering whether the benefits to be realised are sufficiently worthwhile.

If we regard our primary objective of using CAD as achieving savings in design time, we must consider the time taken to process the design both manually and using a computer. We have already seen that the computer can only be used effectively where the calculation sequences are clear and unambiguous. For any application it is therefore important to identify where this is the case and where less well-defined procedures are used. Clearly, the greater the proportion of calculation the greater the potential benefit of using a computer, although, as discussed in Chapter 2, interactive computing enables problems in which the formal calculations are interspersed with less formal procedures to be effectively treated. Problems in which the calculations are very complex or repetitive result in even greater benefit from using a computer, but as we have seen, even relatively simple procedures can be treated in this way to advantage. Further advantages are realised where standard data can be incorporated within the program as discussed in section 2.1.2.

It is of course important that the potential advantages and savings are not matched by the effort required to use the computer and the program. There are in fact very many examples which are suitable for application on a computer and many of these can be most appropriately tackled on a micro. Not only do they provide an inherently interactive facility but they are also easy to use, making even relatively simple calculations worthwhile. There are few design procedures, therefore, which could not benefit from being treated in this way. Even during the early stages of design when neither the problem nor the calculation procedures are well-defined, a micro could be used to explore potential solutions by incorporating simple 'rules of thumb' into a 'what if?' sequence as shown in Fig 6.9.

In this example the calculations would be much simplified, with bending moments, for instance, being calculated on the basis of load multiplied by span divided by an appropriate factor depending upon the support conditions. Sizes of structural members may be estimated by simple rules of thumb such as span/depth ratios, but a facility is also provided whereby some dimensions can be specified, placing additional constraints on the subsequent calculations. It may be appropriate to include a rough cost estimate for comparison purposes, although this would not of course be an accurate figure.

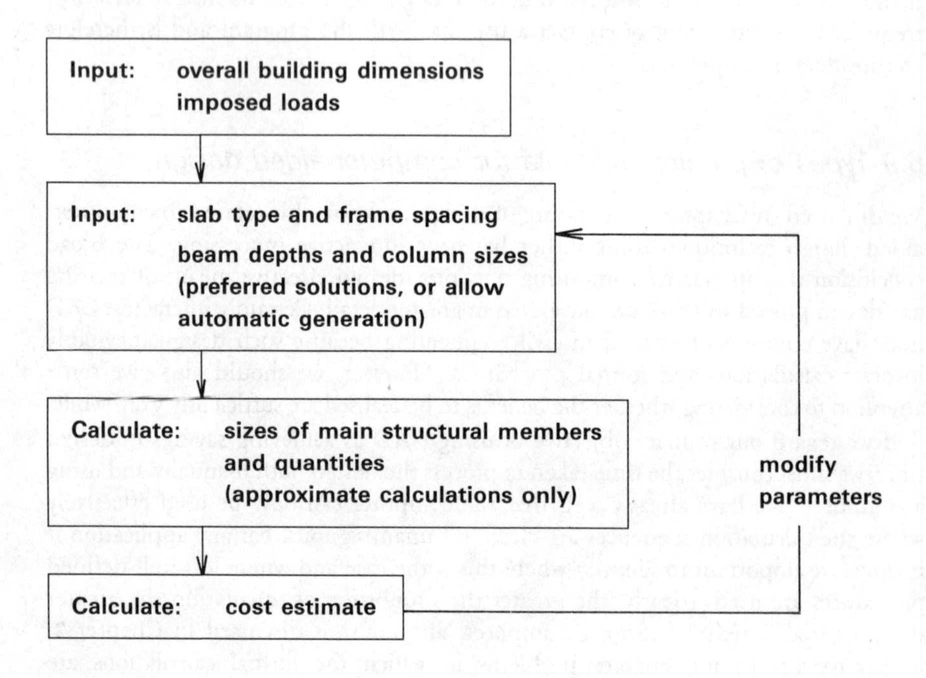

Fig. 6.9 The scheme of a program allowing rapid exploration of the influence of various design parameters on the final solution.

6.10 A summary of the features of good quality software

The success of any CAD facility is clearly highly dependent on the quality of the software. For microcomputers, the essential features of good software are the ease with which the program can be used and the degree to which it exploits the interactive nature of the hardware. More specifically, the communication between the user and the screen should be in a uniform conversational style, easy to use for someone who has little knowledge of computers. Displays, whether results or prompts for data input, should therefore be clear and concise, and neatly formatted. Full checking and editing facilities should be provided and modifications should be capable of being effected quickly and easily. Where appropriate, graphics should be used to facilitate the interpretation of results or data checking, and default values included to minimise the effort of data input. A facility for saving the data on a disc file is very useful in providing for the possibility of subsequent modifications, and the printed output should be suitable for independent checking. Finally, the documentation should be clear in terms of both what the program can and cannot do, and how to use it.

Chapter 7

Microcomputer disc systems

As we said in Chapter 3 and emphasised further in Chapter 4, the amount of internal RAM available to the user is finite, yet we may require to use programs or data sets which exceed internal memory. In Chapter 4 we outlined how a floppy disc mass store can be used and that a disc operating system (usually CP/M or MSDOS) is used to make the transfer of programs or data between internal memory and disc as simple as possible.

In this chapter we shall explain how disc files are used and the type of files available for data. For ease of description we shall confine examples to programs written in interpreted Microsoft BASIC operating on a micro with the CP/M operating system.

7.1 Storing programs

The disc-operating system allows a user to 'save' a program on a disc 'file'. Saving a file is simply the process of transferring a program which exists in the computer's internal memory to disc memory and giving it a unique name by which it can be identified. As explained in Chapter 3, if a program has been entered through the keyboard and the computer is turned off, the complete program is lost. Saving a program on disc allows it to be 'loaded' into internal memory when the computer is next used. While we can think of a disc file of a program as a permanent copy, it is only as permanent as the disc itself; if the disc is damaged or lost, so is the program. It is always advisable to keep back-up copies of all discs.

The instructions to save and load are simple. For example, if the program for the simple beam design in Chapter 5 has been entered through the keyboard, the user merely types the instruction SAVE "BEAM" for the program to be stored on disc. The word contained between the quotation marks can be any name chosen by the user to identify the program. The same program can be loaded into internal memory on a subsequent occasion by typing LOAD "BEAM" and can be used. If the program requires modification it may be carried out through the keyboard and may be run as a check. It should be appreciated that the program "BEAM" on the disc is still the original unmodified version. If it is to be replaced by the new version in internal memory, then SAVE "BEAM" will overwrite the old version on disc with the new version.

7.2 Storing data

Most micros allow data to be stored in two types of data file, either a 'Sequential' file or a 'Random Access' file. A number of files may be open at the same time, the access to each file being identified by a unique 'channel' number. In MBASIC this number is usually preceded by the character '#'.

7.2.1 Sequential data files

Sequential files store data (i.e. numbers or text) in a sequential format, i.e. the first item of data is stored first, then the second item and so on, each item automatically separated by a comma. If the different items of data are of different lengths, it is difficult to know exactly where a specific piece of data starts and ends in the file. If we want to read the nth item of data in the file, the sequential file must be read from the beginning and by counting the number of commas (carried out automatically by the micro), the nth item can be retrieved.

Although this is obviously a fairly long process if large data files are being used, there is the benefit that disc file space is used economically because the data is packed end-to-end on the disc.

To demonstrate the program statements required for sequential disc files we shall assume that a program has been written to calculate bending moments and deflections at 20 points along a beam and that this data is to be saved in a file called "RESULTS". We shall assume that the data is stored in two variable arrays in the micro's RAM called BM and DF. The following program statements are necessary:

```
1000 OPEN #1, "O", "RESULTS"
1010 FOR J = 1 TO 20
1020 PRINT #1, BM(J)
1030 PRINT #1, DF(J)
1040 NEXT
1050 CLOSE #1
```

Line 1000 is required to open the disc file channel 1, defines it as a sequential output file ("O") and allocates the name "RESULTS" (or any other suitable name selected by the programmer). The channel number is used in subsequent statements to refer to this particular file. Many separate files may be open at the same time but each would have a separate channel number to refer to the appropriate file name.

Line 1010 starts the FOR...NEXT loop for the 20 points along the beam.

Line 1020 is the instruction to transfer the value of BM(J) to the file associated with channel 1 (file "RESULTS").

Line 1030 transfers the value of DF(J) to the file associated with channel 1.

Line 1040 continues the FOR...NEXT loop.

Line 1050 closes and secures the file "RESULTS".

To read back the results from the data file, lines 1020 and 1030 would be changed to:

```
1020 INPUT #1, BM(J)
1030 INPUT #1, DF(J)
```

As can be seen, the program instructions are relatively simple, and sequential files are to be preferred for small files of data which have no regular or consistent structure.

7.2.2 Random access data files

If a data file is large and data retrieval using a sequential file would take too long, a random access file allows data to be stored at known positions in the file. This allows specific data to be recovered immediately and independently of any other data in the same file. The known positions are referred to as 'records'.

Random access files require considerably more specification than sequential files. Using again the example of saving bending moments and deflections at 20 points along a beam, the following program statements are required:

```
1000 OPEN #1, "R", "RESULTS", 8
1010 FIELD #1, 4 AS M$, 4 AS D$
1020 FOR J=1 TO 20
1030 LSET M$=MKS$(BM(J))
1040 LSET D$=MKS$(DF(J))
1050 PUT #1, J
1060 NEXT
1070 CLOSE #1
```

Line 1000 opens the disc file channel 1, and defines it as a random access file ("R"), allocates the name "RESULTS" and defines a record length of 8 bytes. The record length is the total number of bytes of everything to be written in one record of the file, as explained in the following statement.

Line 1010 This statement defines the fields in the file channel 1 to be used in each record. In our example we want to store the bending moment and deflection for a point J on the beam in the Jth record corresponding to that point. We are therefore storing two real numbers which have single precision values. In random-access files we are able to take advantage of the fact that integer numbers only require 2 bytes, single-precision real numbers require 4 bytes and double-precision numbers require 8 bytes irrespective of the actual number of digits in the numbers. Our single-precision numbers must therefore be allocated to fields within the record by specifying that the first 4 bytes are allocated to the variable M$ and the second to variable D$

Line 1020 starts the FOR...NEXT loop for the 20 points along the beam.

Line 1030 is required to assign to M$ (the first 4 bytes of the record) the value of BM(J). It is at this stage that we are giving an instruction to convert the bending moment into the fielded single-precision variable by converting it with the function MKS$ ('make into' single-precision). A fielded integer would have used MKI$ while a fielded double-precision would have used MKD$.

Line 1040 converts the deflection at point J into the fielded single-precision D$ as described above.

Line 1050 M$ and D$ now contain the bytes of data in readiness for saving on the disc. This line is required for the transfer to disc to be carried out. The data is PUT to channel 1 (the file defined in line 1000) in record number J (the value of J defined by the FOR...NEXT loop).

Line 1060 Data for points 1 to 20 are transferred to the data file.

Line 1070 On completion of data transfer the file opened in line 1000 must be closed. Although this may not be essential until the end of the program, closure of a file at the earliest possible occasion will ensure that the data file has been secured.

The benefit of a random access file is that we now know that, for example, the bending moment for the 15th point along the beam is in the first field of record 15. While the power of a random access file is not fully utilised in the simple beam example, large data files extending to many thousands of records will allow the retrieval of data in exactly the same time (virtually instantaneously) as a very small data file.

The program statements to retrieve data are based on the same principle as those for saving data.

```
2000 OPEN #1, "R", "RESULTS", 8
2010 FIELD #1, 4 AS M$, 4 AS D$
2020 FOR J=1 TO 20
2030 GET #1, J
2040 BM(J)=CVS(M$)
2050 DF(J)=CVS(D$)
2060 NEXT
2070 CLOSE #1
```

In these program statements it is assumed that we want to read the bending moments and deflections from file "RESULTS".

Lines 2000 and 2010 are required for the same reasons as described above.

Line 2020 starts the FOR...NEXT loop for the 20 points.

Line 2030 is the instruction to GET or retrieve the fielded data M$ and D$ as defined in line 2010 from channel 1.

Line 2040 converts the fielded M$ into the single-precision value BM(J). An integer would have required CVI while a double-precision would have required CVD.

Line 2050 converts the fielded D$ into the single-precision value DF(J).

Line 2060 continues the loop for the 20 points along the beam.

Line 2070 closes and secures the data file.

Had the values of only one point on the beam been required, lines 2020 and 2060 would not be used and the value of J would have had to be set to the number of the point on the beam.

Random access files therefore provide a powerful method of saving and retrieving numeric data quickly and in a very compact way. However, if text data is being used, random access files may suffer from under-utilisation of disc space. The reason for this is that the field width for text must be set to the maximum number of characters ever to occur in the text string to be saved. If the actual text is shorter than the field length, the spare spaces are set to blanks and cannot otherwise be used.

Figure 7.1 shows as an example the layout of a random access file storing names. Each record contains a field length of 5 for each person's initials and a field length of 15 for the surname – i.e. a record length of 20 bytes. While the name in the first record uses all 20 bytes, the subsequent names, although shorter, still consume 20 bytes in order to retain the structure of the random-access file. By contrast, Fig. 7.2 shows the same data contained in a sequential file. Although text stored in a sequential file requires additional quotation marks and commas (automatically given by CP/M), it is evident that the data may be stored without any waste of disc space.

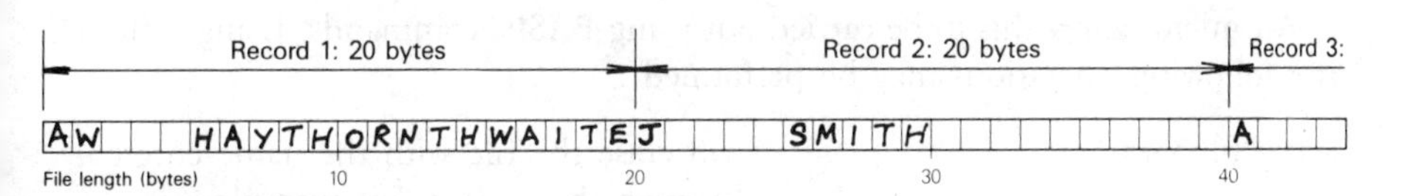

Fig. 7.1 Example of storage requirements in a random access disc file

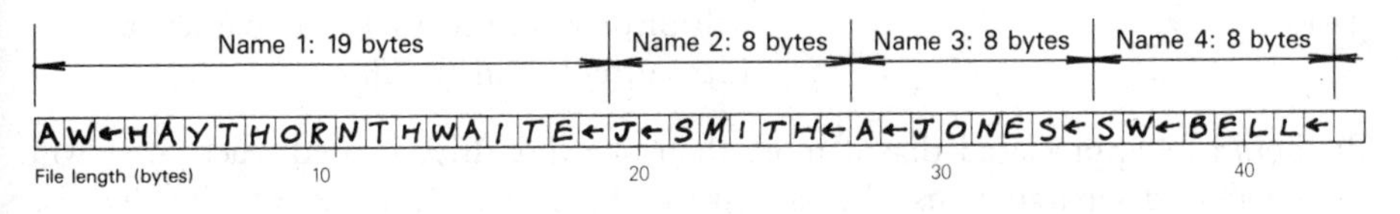

Fig. 7.2 Example of storage requirements in a sequential disc file

The decision whether to use random access or sequential files is usually an easy one to make; large data files with a repetitive structure are considerably more suited to random access, but there is one further problem to be considered which may often unexpectedly waste large amounts of disc space. This concerns the way in which CP/M divides disc space. As explained in Chapter 3, a disc consists of a number of tracks and sectors, each sector typically containing 128 bytes of data. A random access record has its record length specified in the OPEN statement (as in the beam example discussed earlier) and the first record is saved in the first available sector. The second record will also be saved in the same sector only if there is sufficient remaining space in that sector to take the full record length. If that sector cannot take the full record length, the whole of the record is stored in the next sector thereby wasting the space remaining in the first sector.

In our example of saving bending moment and deflection data with a field length of 8 bytes, CP/M can store exactly 16 records in each sector with no space wasted at all. If, however, our record length had been 65 bytes, there would have been 63 bytes of wasted space in each disc sector. Clearly a large data file with a record length of 65 bytes would waste nearly one half of the disc space available. The obvious approach is to ensure that the difference between the sector size and the appropriate multiple of the record length is as small as possible.

7.3 Disc file maintenance

After using a disc for some time it is likely that it will contain a number of old programs and superseded data files. It is often necessary to carry out periodic 'housekeeping' to clear out redundant files to release space for new files.

All micros allow this to be carried out using BASIC commands. Using MBASIC, the following operations may be performed :

KILL "filename"	will erase the file with the name entered between the quotes. For example, KILL "RESULTS".
NAME "filename1" AS "filename2"	will rename existing file entered as "filename1" with the one entered as "filename2". For example, NAME "RESULTS" AS "DATA".
FILES	will display on the VDU the names of all files currently on the disc.

It should be appreciated that if more than one disc drive is used, each drive will be referenced separately, usually as Drive A, B, C or 1, 2, 3, etc. One of the disc drives will always be the current 'logged-in' drive and the computer will always use that drive unless an alternative drive reference is used to prefix a file name. For example, if the logged-in drive is currently A (probably the drive that the system was booted on), then to erase a file on drive B would require KILL "B:filename". By the same reasoning, if the file RESULTS used in the sequential and random access file examples earlier in this chapter is in disc drive B then the filename would have to be specified as "B:RESULTS".

7.4 Processing large amounts of data

There is no doubt that disc systems can expand the limited internal memory of a micro quite dramatically, but processing time can also increase because of the time required to read and write disc data.

If an application program is processing a large amount of data (too much data for available internal RAM) a disc 'work file' may be used to temporarily hold intermediate results. A typical example of this would be a large plane frame analysis which, even using banded matrices, would require too much internal memory for matrix inversion. The program can be written so that intermediate results of inversion are stored temporarily in a random access file until required again when it would be transferred back to RAM.

The principle of a temporary work file should be used whenever an original data file would be in danger of being over-written by data which may subsequently be found to be incorrect or unacceptable.

Chapter 8

Further programming techniques

In this chapter we shall suggest some ways in which the program writer might proceed beyond the development of fairly simple programs for his own use to producing more polished software of a professional standard. For those who wish to write nothing more than simple programs this chapter is therefore not essential, but for the more ambitious it will hopefully provide some useful ideas. Accordingly, it will be assumed that the reader of this chapter has reasonable experience of BASIC, a brief but by no means exhaustive treatment of which was given in Chapter 5, and those new to programming are strongly advised to familiarise themselves with its use before proceeding. There are a large number of textbooks available which deal in some detail with the fundamental aspects of the language and, provided these are complemented by adequate practice, reasonable competence can be achieved quite quickly.

Reference was made in Chapter 4 to the many different versions of BASIC which are currently in use. Unfortunately, whilst these do have a common base, some of the techniques described in this chapter make use of those features of BASIC which tend to differ most from one version to another. Indeed, on some versions a number of these facilities will not be available at all. It has therefore been necessary to describe these techniques with reference to a specific version of BASIC, and the one selected is the same as we used in Chapter 5, namely MBASIC operating under the CP/M operating system. As described in Chapter 4, this is probably the most widely implemented combination (operating system and language) on microcomputers for professional use. Where appropriate, however, reference will be made to alternative instructions for different versions of BASIC. Furthermore, because different manufacturers have implemented CP/M and MBASIC in very slightly different ways, some details will vary from one micro to another. Where specific examples are included these will refer to the Intertec Superbrain, but some indication of the most commonly occurring differences will be given.

8.1 Paging

As described in Chapter 6, interactive computer programs may be thought of as a series of screen displays or pages, in that at appropriate points the screen is cleared and a new set of information displayed. This is equivalent to turning pages in a book and makes for a far more acceptable intercourse between the user and the computer than simply allowing information to scroll up the screen. Clearing the screen is effected from within the program by a simple instruction, similar to:

```
PRINT CHR$(X)
```

where X is the appropriate ASCII code for 'clear screen', and reference should be made to the user's manual for the particular implementation on a specific microcomputer. For example, on the Intertec Superbrain it is equal to 12. (Other BASIC implementations often have a command such as HOME in Applesoft.)

The subsequent information which is to appear on the newly-cleared screen will of course vary from one application to another and from one part of the program to the next. How the information is to be presented will depend on personal preference, how much information is to be displayed and in what form it might best be presented, bearing in mind the rather limited size of display (typically 24 lines, each 80 columns wide). However, some general points can be made, and these are set out below.

8.1.1 Title

Each page should include a brief description of the type of information which the page contains. Generally a one line title is sufficient, but it is useful to present this in the form of a title block which will be similar for each new page. Thus a suitable heading for a page on which data is to be entered for calculating the bending moment on a beam might be:

```
-------------------------------------------------------------------------------
DATA INPUT FOR BEAM ABC1
-------------------------------------------------------------------------------
```

which would have been achieved simply by the program instructions:

```
20 PRINT CHR$(12)
30 PRINT STRING$(79,45)
40 PRINT "DATA INPUT FOR BEAM" ; ID$
50 PRINT STRING$(79,45)
```

Lines 30 and 50 give the instruction to display 79 times the character whose ASCII code is 45 (i.e. a dash). They might alternatively have been written in the form:

```
30 FOR J = 1 to 79
32 PRINT "-" ;
34 NEXT J
36 PRINT
```

or

```
30 PRINT A$
```

where in an earlier program statement A$ had been defined as:

```
10 A$ = STRING$(79,45)
```

Note that in line 40 above the variable ID$ is a string variable previously assigned a name identifying the particular beam being considered. Although displaying the text of the title within an enclosed block does occupy a significant amount of the display space – three lines out of a maximum twenty four in the above example – it does make for easier interpretation by the user if used consistently throughout the program. A simple line of text without enclosure could be used, reducing the space required, albeit at the expense of reducing the visual impact. However, by using techniques such as inverse video (see section 8.3) this problem can be overcome.

8.1.2 Planning the page format

The limited page size makes it essential to plan carefully the way in which the information is to be presented. If a page title block as described above is used, and remembering that one line may be necessary to 'turn the page' (see section 8.1.3) the screen display is reduced to less than 20 lines of 80 characters. Furthermore, in order to facilitate abstraction of the important information it will be necessary to give some explanatory text (including dimensions if appropriate) although it may be possible to incorporate some of this within the title block. Adequate spacing (both horizontally and vertically) should be provided between individual items to avoid a display which would be difficult to read and possibly lead to incorrect values being noted. Most microcomputers now have both upper and lower case letters (earlier Apples provided only upper case which if displayed on adjacent lines looked untidy and very congested) and a reasonable line spacing/character size so that in general information displayed on successive lines is easy to read. Even so, it may be desirable to provide blank lines and spaces to present a satisfactory format, and again the implications on available display space cannot be ignored.

A useful procedure when planning a screen display is to use squared or graph paper divided into the appropriate number of lines and columns to experiment with different layouts. It is of course important when considering this that attention is paid to the range of values which may need to be printed. A display which may appear perfectly satisfactory when a variable has a value of, say, 10 may be extremely confusing when the same variable is equal to 10 000 unless this has been provided.

8.1.3 Ending the page

In the same way that a reader, having finished one page, will turn to the next, so the user requires a facility whereby he can refer to the next screen display. This can be done in a number of different ways and may be implicit in the interactive conversation between the user and the computer for certain types of screen display as will be discussed shortly. At its simplest, however, if the user is presented with a series of results he must have a facility for indicating that he has absorbed the information displayed and wishes to proceed to the next page. This can be achieved simply by a program statement such as:

```
10 INPUT "Press RETURN to continue ",A$
```

which will simply cause the program execution to be suspended until the RETURN key is pressed. This does, however, occupy yet another line of the display, and if the preceding line is left blank, as is often desirable for a better screen format, the number of lines is further reduced. To avoid this the reminder could be incorporated within the title block which may now appear as:

```
RESULTS FOR BEAM ABC1                    (Press RETURN to continue)
```

This can be achieved by simply PRINTing the title and results, and using an INPUT statement without a prompt at the bottom of the screen. Alternatively, a similar effect could be obtained by using the cursor control functions described in section 8.2 to display the input prompt within the title block as shown. Whatever arrangement is adopted, it is important to be consistent in order to avoid confusing the user.

8.1.4 Data input pages

As explained in Chapter 6, all input data should be clearly prompted using the:

```
INPUT "prompt",variable
```

form of data input. With 80 columns available the prompts can be quite detailed but, particularly for an experienced user, lengthy prompts can become tedious. In fact, for simple data input a 40 column display would probably be adequate and it is often convenient to artificially divide the screen into two with the left-hand side used for conventional data input and the right-hand side for warning messages or explanatory details where appropriate. Further possibilities are described in section 8.2.

A typical screen display for data input may therefore appear as:

```
DATA INPUT FOR BEAM ABC1

Span                     (m)  6
Load                     (kN) 20
Distance from lh end     (m)  7   *** DISTANCE > SPAN ***
```

The warning message indicating that the load is off the beam could be emphasised by using inverse or flashing video as described in section 8.3. Note that in this case the data has not been rejected automatically, the implication being that the program may still provide results for this case. The warning message, however, does draw the user's attention to the rather improbable value. If this value is strictly inadmissible, the data should simply be rejected and a new value requested.

On completion of the last item of data input the program can of course automatically proceed to the next screen display without further instruction from the user.

In its simplest form the data input routine would therefore consist of the title block (see section 8.1.1) and the following statements:

```
10 INPUT "Span                                        (m) ",SP
20 INPUT "Load                                       (kN) ", W
30 INPUT; "Distance from lh end                       (m) ", X
40 IF X > SP THEN PRINT "   *** DISTANCE > SPAN ***" ELSE PRINT
```

but for certain reasons an apparently more complex procedure might be preferred and the following sections include further suggested refinements for data input routines. Note that the semicolon immediately after the INPUT statement in line 30 is necessary to suppress the line feed and allow the warning message to be displayed on the same line. The second PRINT command in line 40 produces this line feed if the warning message is not displayed. The IF...THEN...ELSE command which controls this is a useful extension of the IF...THEN command described in Chapter 5. As the words suggest, if the condition following the IF statement is satisfied the instruction immediately after the THEN statement is executed. If the condition is not satisfied, the instruction following the ELSE statement is carried out.

(a) Input of all data as string variables

Most versions of BASIC check that input data for numeric variables is in an acceptable form – i.e. that it is a number and not a string. If it is found that this is not so, a prompt such as INVALID ENTRY! is given requesting the data again. Whilst it may be argued that a serious user would be unlikely to make such a mistake and that even if he did the program run is not interrupted, such an error may upset the screen format, and there are a few instances where either a string (particularly a null string) or a number may be valid. By treating all variables initially as string quantities and subsequently converting them to numeric variables where necessary, checking in the process that this can be done – i.e. that a number has indeed been entered – these small difficulties may be overcome with very little penalty. Thus line 10 above may now read:

```
10 INPUT "Span                                        (m) ",B$
20 GOSUB 1000
30 IF ER=1 THEN 10
40 SP=B
...
...
```

```
1000 ER=1
1010 IF LEN(B$)=0 THEN RETURN
1015 ER=0
1020 FOR J=1 TO LEN(B$)
1030 A=ASC(MID$(B$),J,1)
1040 IF (A > 47 AND A < 58) OR A=46 THEN 1060
1050 ER=1
1060 NEXT
1070 IF ER=0 THEN B=VAL(B$)
1080 RETURN
```

This routine examines each character of the input value in turn (line 1020), converts it into the corresponding ASCII code (line 1030), checks that it is either a number or a decimal point (line 1040), and if all checks are satisfied returns with the variable ER equal to 0 (line 1080). If any of the characters are found to be invalid or if no value had been entered the value of ER is set to 1 and the appropriate action can be taken on returning to the calling routine (line 30).

By making use of this approach, in conjunction with direct cursor addressing (see section 8.2), invalid entries can be trapped and the screen format maintained. Clearly, additional checks can be incorporated, ensuring that the numeric values of data are within specified lower and upper bounds. Similarly, where the user may, as a valid option, enter a non-numeric character (e.g. a null character when pressing RETURN to proceed, or a designated key, say H, to implement the help overlays as described in section 8.4), these too can be checked within a modified version of this routine. Although it would appear to be a lengthy process, in reality the time delay is imperceptible and, by using a general checking routine of this nature, program code is kept to a minimum.

(b) Input of data within subroutines

As will be seen in the next section, editing of data can be carried out very conveniently if the data input statements, together with any appropriate checks, are within self-contained subroutines. Thus the above statements 10–30 might be replaced with:

```
10 GOSUB 250
20 GOSUB 280
30 GOSUB 300
...
...
250 INPUT   "Span                                    (m) ",SP
270 RETURN
280 INPUT   "Load                                   (kN) ", W
290 RETURN
300 INPUT   "Distance from lh end                    (m) ", X
320 RETURN
```

This again appears to result in a much greater number of program statements but, as will be seen from the following section, it does facilitate the organisation of data checking and review.

8.1.5 Data check pages

As discussed in Chapter 6, it is important that all data input is subsequently displayed for positive checking by the user, and this is most easily achieved by reviewing the data in blocks (equivalent to the data input blocks). A typical screen display for data checking may therefore appear as follows:

```
DATA CHECK FOR BEAM ABC1

1 Span                                                    6 m
2 Load                                                   20 kN
3 Distance from lh end                                    7 m

Input number of any incorrect item or press RETURN to continue 3
Distance from lh end                                   (m) 5
```

The routine for this data check would then simply consist of the following statements, together with a title block similar to that described in section 8.1.1:

```
10 PRINT "1 Span                                   ";SP;"  m"
20 PRINT "2 Load                                   ";W;" kN"
30 PRINT "3 Distance from lh end                   ";X;"  m"
40 PRINT
45 INPUT "Input number of any incorrect item or press RETURN to continue ",B$
50 IF B$=" " THEN 100
60 GOSUB 1000
70 IF ER=1 THEN 40
80 ON B GOSUB 250,280,300
90 GOTO 10
100 ...
```

where statements 250 to 320 and 1000 to 1080 given in section 8.1.4 are included. In this way, by writing individual input statements and associated checks within separate subroutines, modifications to that data are simply effected using line 80. It is also worth noting that, although there are a number of ways in which statement 45 could have been arranged, this form requires the minimum of keying by the user.

8.1.6 Results display

Clear display of calculated results is an important feature of any program. A typical display for the calculated bending moments and shear forces for the above example may typically be as follows:

```
CALCULATED BM's (kNm) AND SF's (kN) FOR BEAM ABC1
```

Distance from lh end	BM	SF
0	0.0	250.0
1	225.0	200.0
2	400.0	150.0
3	525.0	100.0
4	600.0	50.0
5	625.0	0.0
6	600.0	-50.0
7	525.0	-100.0
8	400.0	-150.0
9	225.0	-200.0
10	0.0	-250.0

The results have been presented here in tabular form which may often be suitable, particularly since it enables a more condensed display. Whatever the form of the display, it is important to present numerical results to a sensible number of significant figures, and it is again desirable to format the information. The first of these requirements can be achieved in various ways. Most versions of BASIC have an integer function, INT(X), which returns the largest integer less than or equal to X. Although, used directly, this would lead to truncation rather than rounding, it does provide a basis for obtaining a value to a specified number of decimal places. Thus, if X has a value of 8.59451 and it is desired to display this to one decimal place only – i.e. as 8.6 – the following routine could be used:

```
10 X=(INT(X*10+0.5))/10
```

MBASIC also includes a function CINT(X) which directly incorporates this rounding facility. Hence CINT(8.59451) would return a value of 9 and the above statement 10 could be written:

```
10 X=(CINT(X*10))/10
```

In either case the correct number of decimal places can easily be obtained. However, when issuing a PRINT instruction it is the beginning of the number which is positioned (i.e. left-justified) and hence the number of figures preceding the decimal point is important. It is possible to overcome this so that the decimal points are aligned, but the procedures involved are rather cumbersome. More conveniently, the PRINT USING statement can be used. This is not available on all versions of BASIC, but is a very useful facility, corresponding as it does to the FORMAT statement in FORTRAN. For a numeric field the statement takes the form:

```
PRINT USING "###.##";X
```

which states that the variable X will be printed with two figures following and a maximum of three figures preceding the decimal point. The number will also be right-justified regardless of how many digits actually precede the decimal point. A number of other options are available including the printing of strings and exponential numbers in this way.

8.1.7 Menu display

The menu displays by which the user exercises control over the program execution might most appropriately follow a similar form to that of the displays for data checks. Thus a typical menu may appear as follows:

```
BEAM DESIGN PROGRAM – OPTIONS FOR BEAM ABC1

1 Another load case
2 Modify data
3 Select section
4 Print results
5 End run
Select option number
```

By structuring the program as a series of subroutines the selection can again be effected using the ON ... GOSUB ... statement. Thus the corresponding program statements would consist of:

```
10 PRINT "1 Another load case"
20 PRINT "2 Modify data"
30 PRINT "3 Select section"
40 PRINT "4 Print results"
50 PRINT "5 End run"
60 PRINT:INPUT "Select option number ",B$
70 GOSUB 1000
80 IF ER=1 THEN 60
90 ON B GOSUB ...
100 GOTO 10
```

where the routine described in section 8.1.4(a) (i.e. statements 1000 to 1090) is also included. Note that in this case the routine would need to be modified to allow only integer values in the range 1 to 5 to be accepted as valid.

One useful feature of the ON ... GOSUB ... statement is that if the control variable (in this case B) is less than one or greater than the number of alternative options (in this case five) the program simply moves to the next line. Thus line 100 will be accessed immediately only if an option number less than one or greater than five has been selected. Neither is an acceptable value and statement 100 therefore simply refers the user back to the selection of an option number starting in line 10. On completion of the appropriate subroutine, control returns to line 80, and again the user is presented with the available options.

8.2 Cursor controls

It is clear that the screen display is of major importance for interactive programs. It is therefore useful in developing programs to be able to specify where individual items, whether they be text, results or input prompts, appear on the screen. Unfortunately, there is no direct facility for this in MBASIC itself although in some versions of BASIC such as Applesoft, HTAB and VTAB functions serve this purpose. However, the operating system CP/M does provide such a capability through the ESCAPE key. If the screen is considered as a grid 80 spaces across and 24 spaces down, this allows the cursor to be positioned at any of the 80 × 24 possible locations. The details of how this is achieved varies from one microcomputer to another. On the Superbrain the escape character has the ASCII code 27 and the appropriate command would be represented by the statement:

```
PRINT CHR$(27)+"Y"+CHR$(31+J)+CHR$(31+K)
```

where J and K represent the screen co-ordinates and the other characters are machine-dependent.

The use of cursor controls creates many possibilities since it is no longer necessary to input data or print results in a sequential manner starting at the top of the screen and progressing down and to the right. Referring to some of the types of screen display discussed in sections 8.1.4 to 8.1.7, we can consider some examples of how cursor control can be best used.

The form of data input described in section 8.1.4 whereby all data is input as string variables and thorough checks are made upon each item is of course dependent upon the cursor control function, since invalid entries simply result in the cursor returning to its previous position immediately after the appropriate prompt. The remainder of the display is thus unaffected by such errors. It is, however, useful to present a message indicating the nature of any data error, whether it be an attempt to input an illegal character as part of a numeric variable, a non-integer value to an integer variable, or a value which is beyond the predefined limits (specified in the program manual) for that particular item. Such checks can be efficiently included within the routine described in section 8.1.4(a) and if an illegal value is entered an error message is displayed. To avoid disturbing the screen format the cursor control function can be used to PRINT this message at a particular screen location (perhaps within the title block or on the bottom line) before returning to the appropriate part of the screen for a new value to be entered.

Another simple use of the cursor control function in terms of data input is to accommodate multiple input on a single line but, unlike the way described in section 5.10, each item can be provided with its own prompt. Alternatively, following the suggestion made in section 8.1.4 of dividing the screen into two halves, the right-hand side could perhaps be used to provide a simple sketch describing the nature of each of the input variables. More ambitiously, the screen could be displayed as a blank form as shown in Fig. 8.1, the cursor moving automatically to the next box on completion of the entry of the previous item. Doing this makes it very simple to include default values and to display the assumed value in the appropriate location. If the user wishes to overwrite this he can do so by entering a new value in the normal way, whereas pressing the RETURN key causes the default value to be accepted. In this case the routine described in section 8.1.4(a) for checking individual characters of data input can be modified to check for a null string.

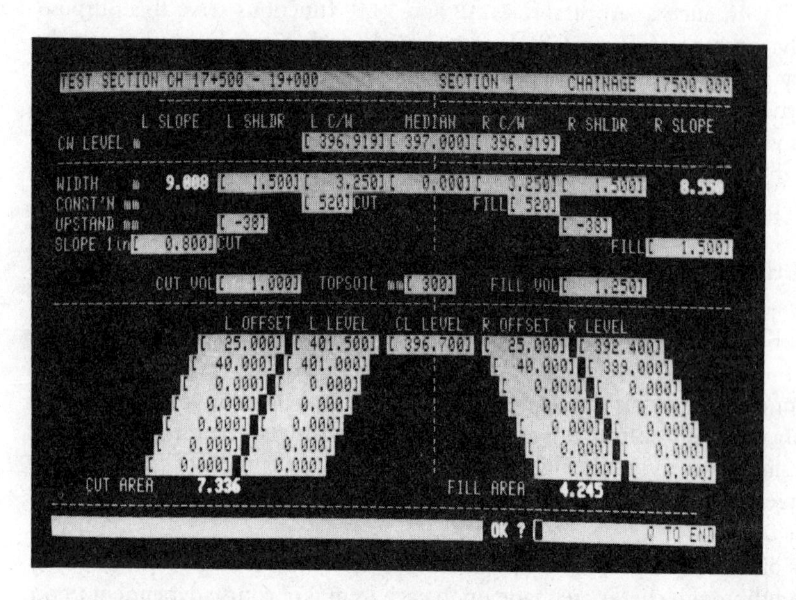

Fig. 8.1 *For some applications, data input pages can be arranged as 'blank forms' allowing easy inclusion of default values (courtesy of Contract Data Research)*

This form of data input also enables the data check to be incorporated on the same display. On completing the entry of all data on the page, the user may proceed to the next section or modify any of the items displayed by pressing the prescribed key. If he elects to change the data the cursor returns to the first item and, in the same way that default values can be incorporated, a new value may be entered or the RETURN key pressed if the displayed value is correct. However, if this technique of combining data input and review is to be used, it is important that the computer displays what it has interpreted as the value input. The value displayed should therefore be PRINTed independently of the value INPUT, albeit in the same screen location, and this is again achieved using the cursor control function.

When displaying results, the benefits of using cursor control are less obvious but, particularly where information is displayed at intervals during a long calculation, it does provide great flexibility in planning the layout of the display. Equally, reference has already been made to the possibility of placing the instruction to proceed within the title block to make more effective use of the limited screen display when presenting results (section 8.1.3). This too can be readily achieved using the cursor control function.

For menu displays the benefit of this facility may also be modest. One technique preferred by some is to display the options and allow the user to move the cursor by simply pressing, for instance, the space bar to move to the next item or the RETURN key to select that item. This corresponds to the arrangements for modifying data described above and can provide clearer instruction to the user.

8.3 Inverse, flashing and dim video

The use of inverse video (black characters on a white screen), and flashing or dim video (designated parts of the screen displayed either as flashing characters or less brightly respectively) can be extremely useful in drawing the user's attention to important parts of the display. As with the cursor control functions, however, no facility exists within MBASIC for these video controls, and it is again necessary to represent the CP/M commands in a similar way to that described in section 8.2. Reference should again be made to the particular microcomputer user's manual for detailed information about how to achieve this. It should, however, be pointed out that not all CP/M microcomputers offer these facilities. The earlier Superbrain I for instance provides neither dim nor inverse video although the later Superbrain II does.

The possible use of inverse video for the title block for each screen display has been mentioned in section 8.1.1. Sensible use of these video controls does enable the user's attention to be drawn to important points – flashing video may be ideal for the type of warning message described in section 8.1.4 – and can thus be of value to the user. These facilities should not, however, be over-used as this can detract from the ease with which information can be assimilated.

8.4 Help facilities

It is often argued that interactive programs require little or no documentation because all actions are screen-prompted. Whilst there is an element of truth in this statement, the provision of large amounts of information can become rather tiresome to a user familiar with the program. Too little assistance of this nature, however, makes it difficult for an inexperienced user. A sensible compromise is to make use of help facilities, although this should not be seen as a substitute for good documentation. Thus, for a particular screen display, the user would be able to press a specified key to obtain some detailed information about the particular features of that display. In the case of data input, this might include more explicit detail concerning individual items, whilst for a results display it may provide clarification of how to interpret the results. The effect of selecting this help option is to cause the original screen display to be temporarily replaced (at least in part) by this additional text, and so this form of display is often referred to as a screen 'overlay'. A typical example of this is shown in Fig. 8.2.

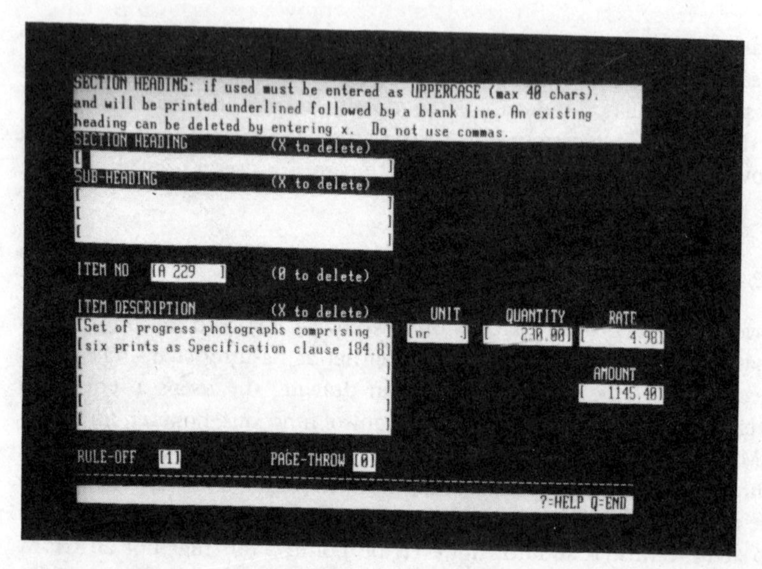

Fig. 8.2 Helpful messages, displayed at the request of the user, obviate the need for constant reference to the program manual without inconvenience to an experienced user (courtesy of Contract Data Research)

This facility could be integrated within the program itself simply as a series of PRINT statements in subroutines, accessed when the appropriate key is pressed. However, this is likely to be a rather inefficient use of the microcomputer's limited memory, and it may be better to include these help overlays as text files on disc.

8.5 Avoiding run-time errors

An abortive program run can be very frustrating and wasteful of a user's time, and all possibility of such a failure should be minimised. The most likely errors are syntax errors, run-time errors and illegal disc operations. The former can be checked most readily by means of a compiler, since with long and complex programs it is otherwise difficult to be sure that every part of a program has been checked by running problems in an interpreting mode.

Run-time errors may occur for a number of reasons. The most common errors are attempting to do something which is mathematically impossible such as dividing by zero, or taking the square root of a negative number. Another common source of such errors is attempting to use a subscript which exceeds the corresponding array dimension. Many potential problems can be avoided by trapping input data which may otherwise lead to errors of this nature and this underlines the importance of the sense and consistency checks which should be applied to all input data (see section 6.4.1).

Many BASICs include an ON ERROR function which in the event of a run-time error direct the program execution to a different part of the program (the error handling subroutine). This routine may include sections designed to identify the cause of the error, and can enable recovery of the run (at least partially). Alternatively, wherever a division or square root is executed involving parameters which could possibly cause problems, use of the IF..THEN command can serve the same purpose. A simple example of this is given below for the solution of a quadratic equation:

```
1100 REM DATA REVIEW
...
...
1200 D=B*B-4*A*C
1210 IF D < 0 THEN 1300
1220 D=SQR(D)
1230 IF A=0 THEN 1330
1240 X1=(-B+D)/(2*A)
1250 X2=(-B-D)/(2*A)
1260 PRINT X1,X2
...
...
1300 PRINT "(b*b-4ac) is negative";
1310 INPUT "Press RETURN to change data ",A$
1320 GOTO 1100
1330 PRINT "a is zero";
1340 INPUT "Press RETURN to change data ",A$
1350 GOTO 1100
```

In this simple example, lines 1210 and 1230 perform the necessary checks to prevent an execution error, and direct the program accordingly if a potential error is identified. Line 1100 corresponds to the beginning of a data review page. By trapping illegal data at input and, where appropriate, using simple routines such as that described above, run-time errors can be avoided without the use of the ON ERROR function.

Illegal disc operations can also cause the premature ending of a program run and should therefore be avoided. The most common causes of this are trying to save information on a disc which is either write-protected or full. The first of these can be checked as a preliminary stage in the run simply by writing and deleting a dummy data file on the disc. If the operation causes an error because the disc is write-protected, the appropriate disc can be replaced. (On some microcomputers, if the disc drive is opened after booting the system, the result is the same as trying to use a write-protected disc, and in this case it is necessary to re-boot the system. Alternatively, a RESET command can be included within the program to allow this function to be performed automatically.)

It is difficult to ensure that there will always be sufficient space available on disc for saving files, but it may be possible to recover from an attempt to write data to a full disc by deleting one or more files from within the program. With this in mind it is good practice to create a dummy file of at least the same size as that to be saved prior to running the program. By including a facility within the program to delete files, space can then be created by removing this when necessary. In a similar way, by using the FILES command, the user can inspect the disc directory to ensure that he is not assigning to a new data file the name of an existing file.

8.6 Economising on memory requirements

Because of the relatively limited memory available on a microcomputer it is good practice to use this as efficiently as possible. This is particularly important where programs are being developed for use by engineers other than the author. Were this not the case it would be possible to omit many of the in-built checks and prompts which are necessary for commercially distributed programs and which may occupy significant amounts of memory. The use of the mass storage facilities (particularly discs) can effectively increase the memory available and this will be discussed briefly in section 8.7. Extending the available memory in this way, however, may introduce significant delays into the processing and, if possible, a program should be capable of operating within the internal memory limitations of the computer. In this section some general advice on condensing programs and memory requirements is given. Ironically, this may be particularly relevant where programs are to be compiled. Although, as described in Chapter 4, compiled programs occupy less memory than the source program together with the necessary interpreter, the process of compilation can be the critical stage in terms of memory. This is because normally the compiler and the source program must both reside within the computer's memory during compilation.

(a) Definition of integers as integer variables

Because integers can be represented by significantly fewer bytes than real numbers, defining any variables which will only assume integer values as such can save a significant amount of memory. This can be done simply by using the % suffix – thus X% will be interpreted as an integer variable – or by using the DEFINT declaration. The statement:

```
10 DEFINT J-K
```

will result in all variables with a name beginning with J or K being treated as integers.

(b) Economising on array space

The minimum value for array subscripts is normally set at a default of zero. This means that an array dimensioned as DIM A(10) requires the memory equivalent of eleven variables to be allocated. In many applications it is more convenient to ignore the zero subscript, in which case a small amount of reserved memory will not be used. Whilst this may not be significant, particularly in one-dimensional arrays, it can be important when using multi-dimensional arrays. Even a two-dimensional array, for example B(100,100), reserves memory equivalent to 10 201 variables rather than the 10 000 which are likely to be used. Of course, it is possible to write the program in such a way that the zero subscript is used but it is often more convenient to use the OPTION BASE command. Thus if the statement:

```
OPTION BASE 1
```

is included, the lowest value of an array subscript is set to one, and memory can be correspondingly saved.

(c) Multiple use of variables

Every variable name requires a unique allocation of memory. Thus, even if a variable is no longer needed it will still occupy memory. Perhaps the most common example of this is the counter in a FOR...NEXT loop, and if the same variable name is used for subsequent loops, the values will simply overwrite that currently assigned to it. This will again reduce the overall memory requirement.

(d) Use of BASIC functions and commands

BASIC contains many functions and commands which could be represented by program code itself. One example, which has already been mentioned in section 8.1.6, is the use of CINT(X) rather than a mathematical expression involving INT(X). In general, if full use is made of the BASIC facilities the program can be written to occupy less space. A good example of this is the IF...THEN...ELSE command which can be used to replace multiple IF...THEN statements.

(e) Use of user-defined functions

In the same way that BASIC functions can be used to economise on memory, the program writer can define his own functions. This may be particularly relevant when representing CP/M commands such as for screen control instructions. By defining functions at the outset, not only programming effort but also memory requirements are reduced. A good example of this is the cursor control function described in section 8.2 which could be defined as:

```
DEF FNCUR$(J,K)=CHR$(27)+"Y"+CHR$(31+J)+CHR$(31+K)
```

and subsequent instructions to display information starting at specific screen co-ordinates can then be written as follows:

```
PRINT FNCUR$(J,K);A
```

where A is the variable whose value is to be displayed.

8.7 Chaining programs

As mentioned in the previous section, the limited memory of the microcomputer can effectively be increased by making use of the mass storage facilities, particularly discs. The use of the disc for reading and writing data has already been described in Chapter 7 and further details of database systems will be presented in Chapter 9. Whilst the ability to automatically access the disc for such purposes is a powerful facility in itself, the potential is increased dramatically when used in conjunction with the facility to run one program automatically from another. A typical sequence may be represented diagrammatically as shown in Fig. 8.3.

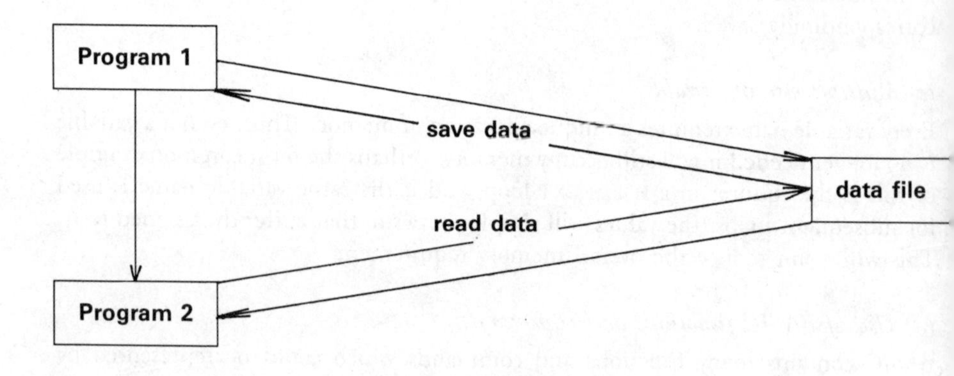

Fig. 8.3 Diagrammatic representation of chaining programs

In this way, if the overall program function can be divided into individual sections (programs 1 and 2 in Fig. 8.3) each of these sections may occupy the full memory available. Thus on completion of the appropriate procedures in program 1, the data required in subsequent sections (program 2) is saved, program 1 deleted from the computer's memory which is then fully available for subsequent use, program 2 loaded, and the necessary data read from the data file. This function is effected through the RUN command, and the program statements could be represented in the following form:

program 1   write data to file (see Chapter 7)
```
100 RUN "PROGRAM 2"
```

program 2   read data from file (see Chapter 7)
continue execution of program 2

A further refinement is possible using the CHAIN command. This clears the current program from memory, and deletes all variables except those declared in a COMMON statement. Thus the same effect could have been achieved in the following way:

program 1
```
10 COMMON variables
...
...
100 CHAIN "PROGRAM 2"
```

program 2
```
10 COMMON variables
...
```

where the variables listed in the COMMON statement correspond to those saved in the data file above. The advantage of this method is that two disc operations, namely saving and reading the data, are avoided, the data corresponding to the variables listed simply not being deleted from memory when the CHAIN command is executed. This results in a certain saving in time which can be significant, but it may be that it is desirable to save the data on file in any case.

Clearly, if chaining between programs is overdone the penalty in execution time can become enormous and the program segments should therefore be planned carefully. Ideally, chaining back to a previous program should be the exception rather than the rule, and it is generally possible to divide even the most interactive design sequence into stages which are unlikely to require frequent referral back to previous parts. Planning the program structure in this way can make best use of the microcomputer's memory, both internal and external, and at the same time allow the program to run without excessive delays due to disc operations.

8.8 Modular construction of programs

Although the internal structure of a program is of little importance to the user, the software developer should strive for a well-planned program since this will facilitate the development itself, and will probably result in a more condensed form. A typical program can be considered as consisting of a control sequence (largely a series of GOSUB statements) and the subroutines themselves, in addition to any declarations for dimensions, common variables or user-defined functions. By planning the program in this form and making liberal use of the REM statement to ease the interpretation of the program statements, it should be relatively straightforward to interpret a program listing in the course of development. A typical structure may therefore be represented as follows:

declarations (user-defined functions, dimensions, constants)
control sequence (calling the appropriate routines listed below)
input routines (arranged in hierarchy)
data check routines
calculating routines
control routines
results display routines
utility routines (titles, etc.)

By making extensive use of the GOSUB statement, these routines can be arranged in separate program blocks, which are neither so small that run-time is seriously affected, or so big that they lose their versatility. For instance, a short subroutine for calculating the bending moment for given conditions is likely to be used in a number of different ways at different stages of a frame analysis program.

8.9 Use of a standard skeleton

Because of the modular construction described above there are a number of blocks which will be common to a wide range of different programs. These could include not only those utility routines, e.g. for displaying titles, but also the main control statements which will be essentially a series of GOSUB statements. By incorporating these within a standard program skeleton, a new program can be developed with a minimum of typing. The extent to which this may be appropriate will vary from from one type of application to another but, having established a consistent style of programming, and particularly if extensive use is made of many of the more advanced techniques referred to briefly in this chapter, the benefits can be significant. We have found that by using this approach new programs can be developed very quickly.

8.10 Installation of programs on different microcomputers

As we have mentioned, different versions of BASIC can differ enormously, although most have similar facilities. Even Microsoft BASIC implemented on different CP/M microcomputers may exhibit minor differences, particularly with regard to control characters. Although a user developing programs may not envisage transfer to different hardware, little effort is required in planning a program to facilitate this. The major differences are as follows:

(a) screen control characters (these include commands to clear the screen, or to position the cursor);
(b) disc instructions (these include the reading and writing of data to data files, the chaining of one program from another, and the ability to carry out limited file operations such as displaying a directory of files or re-naming files);
(c) hard-copy format (this is a function of the printer rather than the computer but, to provide a good standard of printed copy, the output should be paged, and in planning this part of the program it is of course essential to include the number of lines available).

As a general rule, the instructions relating to these functions should be kept within easily identifiable routines, with appropriate variables passed through an install program. Major differences cannot be easily accommodated other than writing in the lowest level of BASIC and this can be very restrictive.

Chapter 9

Database systems

In our discussion so far we have assumed that civil or structural engineers spend their time carrying out computer calculations as part of a design. This clearly is not always the case; our industry envelopes an extremely wide range of activities, much of which is the simple keeping and analysis of records or data. Programs are available on mainframe computers to allow engineers to store information in a 'database' and to access the information selectively, carry out cross-analyses and to produce reports to the format defined by the user.

The advent of microcomputers has also heralded a range of micro database programs which carry out the same type of function as their mainframe counterparts. In this chapter we shall review what is meant by a database system and we shall discuss applications in our own industry.

9.1 A database

A database is simply what the name implies. It is a file of data, usually stored in a computer in a regular and consistent format in such a way that information can be retrieved and processed selectively. The simplest analogy of a computer database is the familiar card-index system used to record and organise data in a predetermined manner.

A card index consists of many cards (we shall call them 'records') on which specific information (data) is recorded in separate positions (we shall call them 'fields'). Taking a simple example of a name and address card index, each record would be one name and address, the first field of each record being the person's name, the second field the first line of address, etc. The last field may be the county of residence. If we wanted to send a standard letter to all people on the index in one particular county we would obviously 'search' through each record and accept or reject the record depending on whether the person lived in the county.

A simple micro database system can replicate the manual procedure by storing name and address records on a disc with the appropriate data in each field and can carry out the search automatically and very quickly. Indeed, the concepts of records and fields suggested here are identical to the meanings of records and fields for random access disc files described in Chapter 7. However, a computer has considerably greater power than that required for searches; for example, the programming required to sort names into alphabetical order is simple and extremely effective and can improve a manual process considerably.

While we may not be too interested in a name and address database, the same principles apply to a wide range of technical and administrative functions required in our day-to-day work. Civil and structural engineering deals with infrastructure for which we need basic inventories. Examples known to the authors are:

(a) *Bridge inventory* – An inventory maintained by highway authorities of each bridge structure recording construction type, age, dimensions, weight limit, road class, services, inspection schedule, etc. The inventory can be 'interrogated' to produce selected listings; for example, a list of all masonry bridges on principal roads greater than 100 years old which have not been inspected within the last twelve months.

(b) *Borehole logs* – A record of all borehole logs giving material classifications, associated test results, Ordnance Survey grid reference, etc. A selected listing could be of test results for Blue Lower Lias Clay found in any borehole within an area specified by OS grid limits. A similar type of database may be developed for laboratory test results of different materials.

(c) *Structural design register* – A record of all designs, for example, of all steel portal frames, recording height, span, loading, crane loadings, estimated cost, final cost, sizes of structural members, date of construction, etc. Quick estimates of structural feasibility and cost can be produced by a selective list of the structural member sizes and final cost of all portal frames of a given range of height, span and loading.

(d) *Highway maintenance* – A record of basic road inventory, construction type, traffic levels, results of standard pavement condition tests, etc. Selective reports may be produced, for example, of sections of road where deflection beam and bump integrator results exceed specified levels in order to determine priority for maintenance works.

The common theme in these examples is the ability to search and then to list records according to the criteria specified by the user.

9.2 Off-the-shelf database systems

While a simple database application can be readily written in BASIC on a micro, there are many benefits in using a commercially available database program. There are now a number of well-tried and proven programs available which will run on a wide range of micros. They all allow the user to set up his own record format (to decide what information is going where), in a similar way to designing a survey sheet. The set-up procedure requires the user to specify the type of information to be entered in each field of the record (text, integer, real number, date, allowable range of input values, etc.) in order that the program can automatically validate data subsequently entered by the user. It also allows certain fields as 'index' or 'key' fields to be used for fast searches.

Once the format of the database has been established, records of data are then entered interactively and checked and validated by the program. Records may subsequently be amended or updated and selected printouts produced according to specified criteria. Some commercial database programs allow some limited cross-field calculation; for example, if a road inventory required the entry of road section length and width, it could (if previously specified) automatically calculate total pavement area for subsequent maintenance costing.

While there are distinct advantages in adopting a commercial database program, it should be accepted that they have a tendency to be all-purpose programs for relatively straightforward record keeping. They are limited in the depth of cross-field calculation, and, of considerable importance, they can be difficult to use. To achieve the full benefit, the user must be fully conversant with the system instructions and the limits of its capabilities. Our experience suggests that careful consideration should be given before adopting such a system if it is only to be used occasionally by untrained clerical staff.

9.3 Purpose-designed database systems

Database systems can obviously vary in complexity from the simple name and address system discussed earlier to an extremely complex highway maintenance priority system to be considered later. We would suggest that, for civil and structural engineering applications, the need for reasonably complex cross-field calculation is of greater importance than the ability of commercial programs to sort records quickly into alphabetical or numeric order.

In this section we shall outline how to approach the construction of a simple database as part of a design process. While we do not profess to be incorporating the best or most efficient programming method or to be adopting the best method of systems analysis, we believe that the engineer can, in fact, produce powerful database programs on a microcomputer.

We shall take, as an example, a simplified bridge structure inventory and assume that the following information is to be stored for each structure under the authority's control; as shown in Table 9.1, each item is given a variable name and maximum number of characters allowed in each field.

Field widths have obviously been chosen to suit the type of data, but have been designed to allow 64 bytes/record. This allows two records per 128 byte sector, thereby ensuring complete utilisation of disc sectors (see Chapter 7), and allowing about 2 500 records to be stored on a standard CP/M micro with double-sided, double-density disc. A program is required to enable a user to enter the above data into the micro and to save the data on a disc file. As discussed in Chapter 7, there are two types of file at our disposal: sequential and random access. Since we are likely to use the data file for a large number of structures, data for which is unlikely to fit into spare RAM, and will want to access individual records selectively, we shall elect to use a random access disc file.

Table 9.1 Variable names and field widths

		Variable name	Field width
(a)	Bridge reference number	RF$	5
(b)	Bridge name	NA$	27
(c)	Road Class	RC$	1
(d)	Road Number	RN$	5
(e)	Year of Construction	YC$	4
(f)	Construction type	CT$	4
(g)	Carriageway width	CW$	5
(h)	Weight limit	WL$	5
(i)	Date of last inspection	DT$	8
	Total record length	64 bytes	

The order in which structures are entered is of no concern to us, therefore details of the first structure available may be saved in record one of the random access file, the next structure in record two, etc. Although this is the simplest approach, we obviously need to know the record number of each structure in order to retrieve its details for subsequent up-dating or amendments.

When the data has been saved in the random access file we require a program which can produce selective reports. This program would allow the user to define a 'search mask' – i.e. to define which variables are to be used to accept or reject records and to define minimum and maximum values of variables in the mask. For example, a report listing full details of all masonry bridges (with the code 'MASN' as its construction type) with a weight limit exceeding 20 tonnes on 'A' class roads would require the data shown in Table 9.2.

Table 9.2 Search Mask

	Variable name	Minimum value	Maximum value
Bridge reference	RF$	–	–
Bridge name	NA$	–	–
Road Class	RC$	'A'	'A'
Road Number	RN$	–	–
Year of Construction	YC$	–	–
Construction type	CT$	'MASN'	'MASN'
Carriageway width	CW$	–	–
Weight Limit	WL$	20	–
Date of inspection	DT$	–	–

The report program would then search each record in turn, starting at record one and, if the data fitted the mask (i.e. each variable in the record would be compared with the minimum and maximum values in the mask), the record details would be printed. Obviously the printout would be in the order in which records had been entered into the database, although an additional part of the program could sort records into a specified order.

This simple database would be extremely effective; the report options would allow any combination of variables to be defined in the mask. However, the report program may be quite slow if there is a large number of structures, and we may decide that one or more variables will always be required in the mask. To improve processing time it is possible to set up a variable 'index' for fast searches. A variable index would be a separate data file which, for each value of a variable, would contain the number in the main database of each record with the variable value. For example, if record numbers 18, 29, 132, 184 are of bridges with a construction type 'MASN', then a separate index of constuction type 'MASN' would contain the numbers 18, 29, 132, 184. Another construction type index 'PSC' would contain the numbers of the records for all prestressed concrete bridges.

When a selective list of construction types is required, the program would first read the index for each type of construction required and would then know where to find the records in the database without having to scan all records. The record would be retrieved from disc and compared with other mask values, to determine whether it should be printed.

While the use of indexes is relatively easy, we believe that it is only essential for very large databases. If a purpose-designed database to be written in interpreted BASIC is too slow to process a file, it is far easier to compile the interpreted program (if a compiler is available for the particular BASIC being used) which will improve processing time dramatically (see Chapter 4).

9.4 Databases linked to the design process

Although basic inventory systems are extremely useful, there are several applications in design where we can use the database principle.

We shall take, as an example, a program to carry out earthwork volume calculations for a new road based on a road cross-section database. The same principles apply to many areas of design which involve repetitive calculation of the same type of data.

In its simplest terms, the volume of earthworks of a new highway is a function of the cross-sectional areas of earthworks cut and fill at regular chainages and the distance between the cross-sections. The cross-sectional areas are determined by the envelope bounding the road formation level, the embankment or cutting sideslopes and the existing ground. A database consisting of the following determines each cross-section:

Chainage
Finished centreline and channel levels
Construction depth

Pavement and verge widths
Embankment or cutting sideslope
Existing ground levels and offset from the road centreline

This limited data is all that is needed for an approximate calculation of cross-sectional area of cut or fill, although more details could be added to produce accurate quantities. A data input program would be required to enter this data for each cross-section in turn and the data could be saved on a disc file using the principles discussed in Chapter 7. However, whilst the data is being entered, the program can also calculate the cross-sectional area immediately (also offsets and levels sufficient for setting out the limits of the earthworks) which may also be saved in the same file on the disc.

The result of this is a database which gives all information relevant to each cross-section. A separate program can then be used to interrogate the disc file to list cross-sectional details (including setting-out data) between specified chainages, or to calculate earthworks volumes and mass-haul from cross-sectional areas and chainage intervals. However, the real benefit arises from the ability to amend the cross-sectional details in the database (for example, to try a different vertical alignment, or to replace existing ground levels with actual levels agreed on site) without having to re-enter all data. Similarly, the ability to select cross-sections on the basis of specified criteria allows, for example, forward or backward processing between alternative chainages to explore and minimise mass haul costs.

This principle is incorporated in a very much more sophisticated form in a program called MROAD and linked automatically to a vertical alignment design program. The database uses 256 bytes for each cross-section containing sufficient data to proceed from an initial estimate of earthworks costs at feasibility design stage, through to final measurement. One disc on a standard CP/M system is capable of storing a database for about 60 km of new highway.

The limits of possible database applications on microcomputers have not yet been reached. Obviously floppy discs have allowed the problems of limited user-RAM in the micro to be overcome, but the limited capacity of a floppy disc can be overcome by using more than one floppy disc or a hard disc to extend the database. One of the most complex database systems of interest to highway engineers is a highway maintenance management system known as SYSTEM BSM described in Snaith, Burrow and Orr (1982) which can operate on a standard CP/M micro with floppy discs.

While we would not suggest that engineers should attempt to develop their own programs for such a complex procedure, these applications demonstrate that a micro is capable of serving an extremely wide range of computing needs.

Figure 9.1 shows how SYSTEM BSM uses floppy discs to develop a library of maintenance data. Each maintenance district in each province or region of a country has one disc on which is recorded the description, basic survey information, road condition and machine results (bump integrator, etc.) for each 250 m section of paved road. The capacity of the system is therefore totally flexible; extra discs for additional maintenance districts will immediately expand capacity. When the annual maintenance budget is to be allocated, each data disc is processed to determine which sections of road exceed pre-set critical levels of deterioration. It recommends and

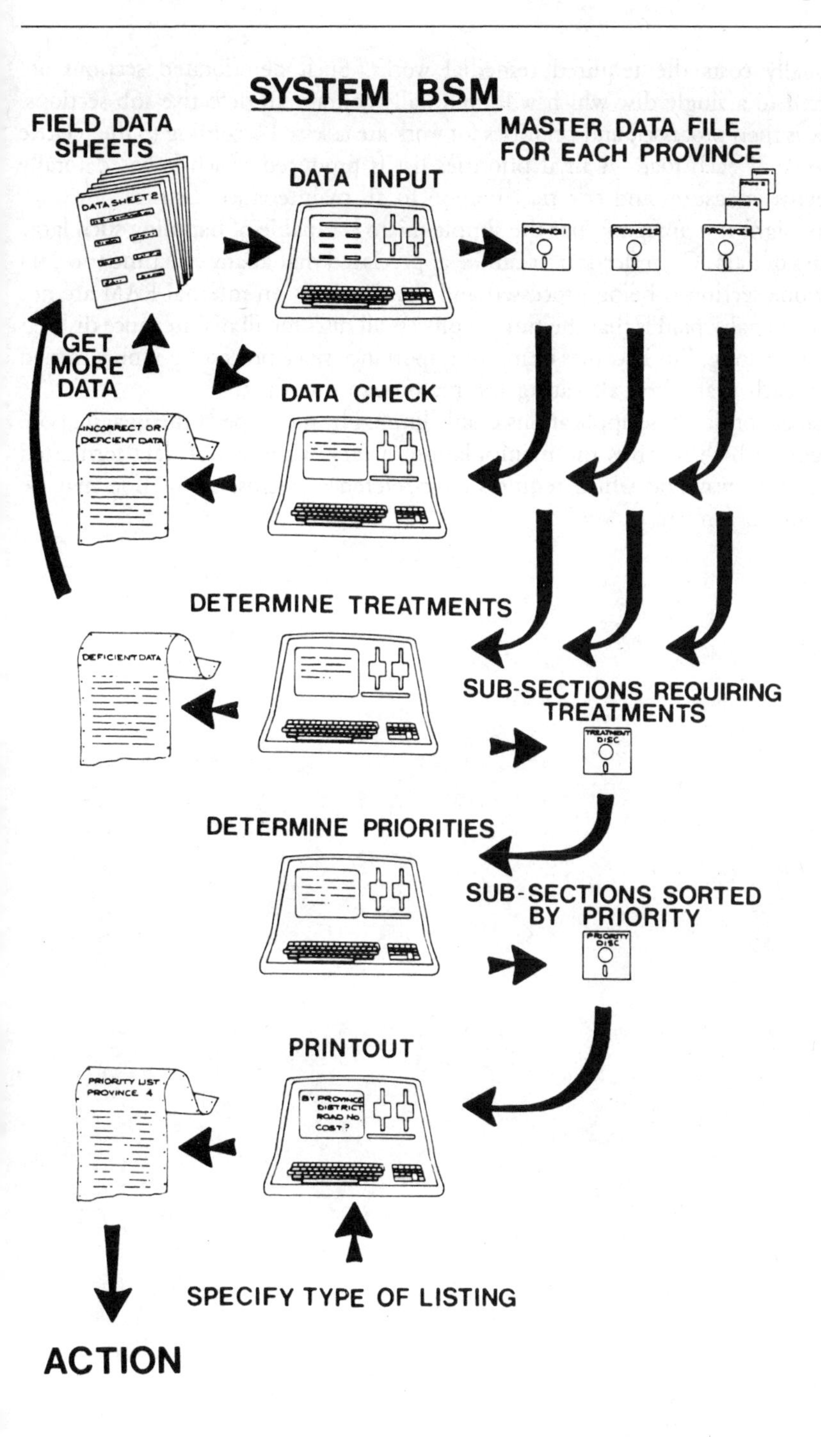

Fig. 9.1 How SYSTEM BSM uses floppy discs to store and process road maintenance data (courtesy of Highway Management Services Ltd)

provisionally costs the required remedial works. Such deteriorated sections are transferred to a single disc which will eventually contain all defective sub-sections. This disc is then processed and priorities for work are assessed according to the relative importance of each road. A final priorities list is produced which is based totally on objective measures and criteria common to all maintenance districts.

At first sight it is amazing that the simple micro is capable of handling such large quantities of data. On reflection, it can be appreciated that at any one time the data for only one section is being processed and the demands on internal RAM are not great. The penalty paid is that the time to process all discs for all maintenance districts may be quite long, but becomes of minor importance since processing is only carried out once each year when allocating the maintenance budget.

The range for database applications is only limited by the scope of the imagination. Any process which involves the manipulation of large amounts of data formatted in a consistent way and which requires cross-reference or cross-calculation may be carried out on a micro.

Chapter 10

Setting up a system

In this chapter we shall attempt to suggest how individual engineers or organisations might proceed in identifying their computing needs, evaluating possible solutions and implementing their final selection of a microcomputer system. It is not intended to be a rigorous step-by-step description, but rather suggestions as to how this task may be approached. Every firm will have its own peculiar requirements and much will depend on the type and volume of work normally carried out, current internal organisation and so on.

This task can be roughly divided into three or four stages. The first stage involves preliminary work, largely in the form of a desk study which will seek to identify the needs and the resources available. The next stage should be to study what software is required to satisfy these needs, identify sources of appropriate programs and evaluate the suitability of each. This should enable the selection of a system, and highlight any restrictions on the type of hardware which is required. Whether or not to proceed with the purchase of the system will probably require justification, and once a positive decision has been reached the system must be implemented.

By spending a reasonable amount of time and effort on this process, it should be possible to arrive at a solution which is going to be a success. On the other hand, failure to plan adequately can result in a system which is an expensive white elephant, confirming the views of those sceptics who believe that computers, and microcomputers in particular, have no role in their work.

Fortunately, the people who have to go through this important exercise need not do so on their own. Help is available, and not all of it is expensive. Some useful sources of such assistance are included.

10.1 Preliminaries

It is important that a certain amount of preliminary work is done prior to assessing alternative systems. Perhaps the most important part of this is to establish clearly the computing needs of the firm, and these should include both technical and non-technical work. Word-processing for instance is often found to be of such benefit in itself that a second installation may be quickly considered to cope with the unexpectedly high volume of such work. Likewise, financial planning and management systems, including payroll and accounts, can often be successfully implemented on a microcomputer.

10.1.1 Needs

In assessing the computing needs, it is appropriate to consider all the work which is currently done by members of the firm. The nature of each item of work should be identified, together with a note of who is responsible for doing it, how much time each person may devote to it, how much repetition is involved, and how often the task is carried out.

It is of course important to establish if the task is suitable for a computer. Some, such as meeting clients or site supervision, clearly are not and can be dismissed immediately, while those which involve significant amounts of calculation might be ideally suited to computer application. Others, such as drawing, belong rather less clearly to one category or the other, but at this stage it should be sufficient to include only those which are obviously suitable.

Although a formal cost-benefit analysis is unlikely to be feasible, it is useful if some idea of current costs of certain types of operation can be assessed. These figures should not be regarded as definitive but a broad indication of how much cost is associated with individual activities can be valuable in identifying the possible solutions to computing needs. Included in this cost analysis should be the current charges incurred by using existing computing facilities such as bureaux.

10.1.2 Benefits

It is even more difficult to establish the potential financial benefit to be gained from using a microcomputer for a particular application. An estimation of time savings may be possible when considering individual items but there are other less tangible benefits which are not easily quantified. These include a shorter turnround for work, with clients receiving a more rapid service. Similarly, modifications can be dealt with almost instantly. This may be particularly important in a competitive tender situation and, in this context, a wider range of alternatives can be considered, allowing some degree of optimisation. This may not necessarily be done in a formal sense, and reasons why this should perhaps be avoided were discussed in section 6.2, but greater opportunities to explore different possible solutions should result in better designs. Similarly, since the engineer is relieved of much of the mundane calculations he should find greater time both to formulate his initial concept and to reflect on the final detail. Both are areas where errors are made, and the failure of designs may often be attributable to these rather than mistakes in the more formal calculation stage of the design process.

A microcomputer is likely to be used not only effectively, but also more readily than many other computer facilities. Compared with other less user-friendly installations microcomputers are easy to use and as such are likely to be used more frequently than current facilities, particularly bureaux. Similarly, if individual organisations have specific applications for which they require to develop software in-house it is often easier to do so on a microcomputer than on a larger computer, even if the latter is provided with readily accessible interactive terminals.

The effect of simplifying the design process by employing microcomputers also has a beneficial effect on staff morale, and may make it easier to employ good quality personnel. Similarly, the effect on potential clients of an apparently modern efficient office making use of the latest technology should not be ignored, although neither of these last two benefits can sensibly be quantified.

10.1.3 Specific requirements

As a result of this exercise in studying and quantifying (where possible) existing activities, it should be possible to identify, in broad terms, those aspects of routine work which may be suitable for application on a microcomputer. It may also highlight any specific requirements for the system. These might include one or more of the following:

(a) Graphics facilities

As has already been suggested, the use of graphics can in some cases provide an ideal display of information, either for checking data such as the input for frame geometry, or for displaying results such as the bending moment diagram for a structure. Of course, for such applications a graphics display is not essential but rather a desirable facility. There are, however, some applications which would be meaningless without a graphical display, and in civil and structural engineering the most obvious example is draughting. Computer-aided draughting is a major topic in itself, and the great majority of packages currently available are not suitable for microcomputers. We will not therefore pursue this, but clearly, if the activities of a firm require graphical output, it is important that the selected system is capable of providing this facility.

(b) Memory and mass storage requirements

Some applications, for example finite element analysis and highway design, may require large programs and/or large volumes of data. It may be that such requirements make microcomputers unsuitable for these purposes, although the development of 16-bit microcomputers with greatly increased memory is important in this context and may enable certain systems to carry out work of this nature, albeit on a somewhat limited scale. Similarly, most microcomputers can be fitted with hard discs, dramatically increasing the mass storage availability. In this respect it is also important to recognise that some apparently similar microcomputers may have significantly different disc capacities. The Superbrain microcomputer for instance is available in three versions with disc capacities ranging from approximately 170K to four times that amount. However, for most of the applications described herein and those representing the routine work in a typical design office, a 64K RAM microcomputer with twin disc drives is likely to provide adequate memory for program and data.

(c) Precision

Most microcomputers work to seven significant figures, although facilities do exist for increasing this at the expense of slowing down the processing speed and increasing the memory requirements. For routine work, however, normal precision is almost certainly adequate, bearing in mind the points made in section 4.3.

(d) Processing speed

Although simple calculations will be processed very quickly, iterative calculations or those involving very complicated operations may be quite time-consuming. In such cases it is usually possible to leave the computer running whilst the user attends to other duties, and the relatively slow processing speed of the microcomputer is no more than an inconvenience. Whilst this would not be possible for an essentially interactive design sequence, for some problems such as frame analysis the work can be treated in a manner equivalent to batch processing. However, in real-time applications, in which time-dependent behaviour is involved, processing speed may be of major importance and will influence very strongly the selection of the system to be used. Again, for all but specialised applications, such considerations are of minor importance.

(e) Use of the microcomputer as a terminal

Potentially one of the most efficient ways of introducing computing into a design office is to use a microcomputer which can also act as a terminal to a larger computer, either in-house or through a bureau. In this way the routine work can most effectively be carried out on a microcomputer acting as a stand-alone facility, independent of any other system. For the occasional problem – e.g. finite element analysis or very large plane frame design, for which the microcomputer is inadequate either because of its limited memory and speed or perhaps because of the unavailability of suitable software – the microcomputer can be linked via telephone lines to a remote computer and used as a terminal. This is effected via a modem which converts the signal from the output of the microcomputer into a signal suitable for transmission on a normal telephone connection. A similar device reconverts the signal at the opposite end before onward transmission to the main computer. In this way information such as data files can be prepared independently using the microcomputer. Then, by issuing the appropriate commands when connected, this information can be transferred very quickly. This offers two advantages, namely the ability to enter, check and review data in an interactive mode, and the need for only a short connect time and hence reduced telephone charges. Raw results can similarly be obtained and subsequently converted into a more appropriate form (post-processing). In this way the user is able to enjoy the benefits of both the large computer on which big complex problems can be handled, and a small dedicated facility more suited to routine work. Fortunately, most microcomputers can now be used as terminals, although there may be difficulties in communicating between specific microcomputers and particular types of larger systems. If this facility is required it should be investigated in detail to establish such restrictions at this early stage.

10.1.4 Budget

In the great majority of cases the particular hardware requirements described above will not be important or it may not be possible to identify them until the software has been investigated. It is fortunate that for most organisations hardware requirements can be met by a very wide range of microcomputers, and in the next section we will therefore concentrate on an assessment of the software. However, before doing so, one final point should be covered at this preliminary stage. This concerns the budget which is available for setting up the system. It is probably a good idea to adopt a flexible attitude towards this, and certainly not divulge an upper limit on expenditure to any adviser or salesman – they will naturally work a system up to that figure. It is better to have a broad idea of what funds might be available as this may well discount some potential systems. The cost and benefits of implementing a system can then be analysed and the most appropriate system selected. It is always advisable to incorporate a degree of expandability into a computer system if possible. Whilst expansion of a microcomputer system may simply mean buying another independent installation, many systems are now capable of being extended. This may include increasing internal and external memory, and providing a network with several terminals sharing common facilities. This potential for extending the installation should not be overlooked, although in most cases the micro will be used as a stand-alone facility.

10.2 Software

In many ways the identification and evaluation of software is the most important part of setting up a system. Indeed, restricted availability of software may often dictate the particular hardware required. Unfortunately, it is not uncommon for firms to be persuaded by slick salesmen to buy a particular microcomputer, only to find that there is little or no suitable software available on it. It is easy to be led to believe that such software will shortly be available, but it is wise to treat such promises sceptically.

10.2.1 Sources of software

The preliminary work undertaken and described in the previous section should have identified a number of possible activities suitable for computer application and some tentative priorities. For instance, a firm which deals largely in the design of buildings will have quite different software priorities from one specialising in highways. For each of the applications, as many possible sources of software should be identified. In general, programs can be purchased off-the-shelf, written in-house, commissioned by the firm from a software specialist, or standard packages may be capable of being customised. For some applications, program listings are available and these can then be typed into the computer. However, apart from the time needed for such a task, this approach is full of potential dangers. In particular, apart from keying errors which will inevitably occur, there may be bugs in the program itself. Debugging programs written by another author is extremely difficult and tedious, and is not something which an inexperienced computer user should attempt.

10.2.2 Commercial programs

Probably the focus of attention will be on commercially available software and there is an increasing number of firms marketing such software for micros. Current information can be obtained from technical journals which carry regular small advertisements for software and good microcomputer retailers should also be able to indicate potential sources of programs. Some of the computer manufacturers also produce details of programs which can be purchased for their range, recognising that potential buyers are now looking carefully at software availability rather than relying on the claims made about the hardware capabilities. Independently-published catalogues are marketed although their emphasis is often on general business applications such as accounts and word-processing. Exhibitions also tend to be rather too general and are often aimed at selling hardware or marketing commercial or business, rather than specialist or technical, packages. However, more specialised exhibitions can be valuable. These enable a number of systems to be seen up and running and compared in a short space of time, although a short demonstration can give a quite misleading impression of a system's quality. Informal contacts may also be a fruitful source of information; other firms doing similar work and local small computer clubs, for instance, may be able to offer information relating not only to sources but also to their own experience of a particular package.

For all suitable commercial programs a brief description of the capabilities, costs, and hardware requirements should be obtained. This will enable a preliminary assessment to be made and a strategy can begin to develop. In evaluating programs the following points should be considered:

(a) Program function

The program should of course be capable of doing the required work. It may not be necessary for it to cope with every eventuality and every possible example of the type of problem which it is designed to solve, but this should not matter ; a '90 per cent solution' may be better – i.e. if a program is capable of being used for the great majority of cases, it may be perfectly adequate. Indeed, we argued in section 6.1.2 that such a solution may be preferable.

(b) Ease of use

In order to be cost effective the program must be easy to use. This will not only enable the program to be used more quickly but it will also encourage its own use and minimise errors. Although this can only be assessed realistically by using the program, some indication can be obtained from the documentation, which should include a description of how the program is to be used.

(c) Reliability

It is difficult to assess the reliability of a program other than through continuing use and monitoring after purchase. However, it is valuable if another firm with experience of the system can be contacted and asked to express an opinion on the program's reliability. The software supplier should be prepared to release the names of previous clients who are willing to do this.

(d) Cost

It is important to know not only how much a program costs, but also what is included for the price. Although it will be implicit that the right to use the program is purchased, documentation, training (if necessary or available), regular updates, and multiple copies may be extra. Of course, it is only to be expected that bargain programs, bought perhaps through mail order, are likely to include less than software purchased from a supplier prepared to offer a better service, both before and after sale.

(e) Technical support

From time to time queries will arise with the operation of the program, and the support and its cost, if available, should be ascertained at this stage.

(f) Demonstrations/trials

By this stage the front runners will probably have been identified and one system will be emerging as favourite. While the above information can be obtained from a desk study, no decision should be made without at least seeing the system in operation and preferably using it in-house. The latter may involve a modest fee but this is often returnable in the event of an order to purchase and in any case it is well worth doing. It is really the equivalent of a test drive in a new car. The points discussed in Chapter 6 may be helpful in compiling a checklist to assess the performance of software in this context.

Because of the problems of transportability between different microcomputers it is unlikely that a buyer will be able simply to establish the most suitable programs for each particular application and purchase these together with the necessary hardware. It is more likely that a compromise will be necessary, with the favoured program for different applications being available on different makes of microcomputer. Nevertheless, provided that the preliminary work has been adequately prepared, and possible future needs are accounted for, it is unlikely that major errors will occur since the choice should have been narrowed down to only those alternatives which are most suitable. Microcomputer systems represent a relatively modest investment and this can normally be recovered quite quickly, even if the right system is not selected.

10.2.3 Purpose written and customised programs

For many of the common routine design applications a range of good software is now available. Compared with the cost of developing a program in-house the prices charged for these are generally very attractive. For less common applications, however, there may be deficiencies in the programs on the market; the quality may not be good, the range of suitable hardware may be very limited, or there may simply be no programs at all. Under these circumstances, the alternatives are to commission a program or to develop it within the firm. In either case the costs are likely to be considerable even for apparently modest tasks. However, it may be that in some cases this cost can be justified because of the volume of work concerned with the specific application, or that costs can be shared by co-operation with other organisations concerned with similar activities.

In some cases, commercially available programs may meet most of the requirements but be deficient in certain details. A possible solution here is to approach the program author with a view to customising the program to suit individual needs and, depending on the changes necessary, this may not be an expensive exercise.

For smaller tasks, the cost of program development in-house may not be excessive, and we have already indicated that the designer is the most appropriate person to establish the structure of a program. Software development in-house should not therefore be seen as inappropriate, but clearly any activity of this nature must be carefully planned and managed.

10.3 Final assessment

10.3.1 Cost-benefit analysis

Having completed the survey of available software (and hardware) and identified the favoured solution it will probably be necessary to provide some cost-benefit analysis in order to justify the purchase. This is not always easy because, as mentioned above, the benefits are often not capable of being defined in accounting terms. Nevertheless, savings in engineers' time is likely to be the main reason for purchase and an estimate of the comparison between the current cost (design time, bureau charges, etc.) and projected cost using a microcomputer should be made.

Costs will be easier to quantify and will of course include capital expenditure on hardware and software, and fixed recurrent costs such as insurance and maintenance. It is more difficult to estimate running costs associated with engineers' time and, to a much lesser extent, the cost of consumables, particularly printer paper and discs. Nevertheless, by making sensible predictions, some broad indications can be obtained and costs apportioned accordingly. In the final analysis, the decision to proceed or not is unlikely to made on the basis of a formal cost-benefit study, but the exercise should hopefully provide the basis for a reasoned discussion.

10.3.2 Hardware

We have suggested that the software selection should dictate the hardware requirements rather than vice-versa. Following this route, the hardware will often be selected automatically. Nevertheless, it may be that alternative systems are possible either utilising different software or – as is increasingly the case with microcomputers running under the CP/M operating system – the same software installed on different microcomputers. In either case the supplier should be asked to give information on a number of points, including availability, delivery period (both for demonstration and purchase), the names of others currently using similar equipment, provisions for coping with machine faults (repair facilities, loan arrangements and maintenance agreements), what improvements or upgrades might be expected in the near future, whether the equipment is capable of such upgrading and if so at what cost.

10.3.3 Tax implications

Computers and associated equipment are classified as 'capital investment' and can attract appropriate income or corporation tax relief, the amount depending on the individual circumstances. In general, a business can elect to choose a 100 per cent first year capital allowance or an annual written-down allowance for hardware purchased outright or on a hire purchase agreement. The value of the allowance would depend on the marginal rate of tax paid by the business. If the hardware is leased, no capital allowance can be claimed (it would be claimed by the lessor), but the leasing payment would be an allowable expense in the trading or profit and loss account.

10.4 Implementation

Compared with the preparatory work necessary before the installation of a large computer, the installation of a microcomputer requires little effort. However, there are certain aspects of this which should be well prepared if the system is to be used effectively and successfully. As far as the operating environment is concerned, a typical office is perfectly adequate and no special provision need normally be made. If the microcomputer is to be used overseas, it may be necessary to ensure that the levels of temperature and humidity are acceptable, and, perhaps more important, that the electricity supply is sufficiently stable. Sudden peaks or troughs in the supply voltage can occur and cause the program to fail, although they are most unlikely to cause damage to the hardware. Supply voltages overseas may be more variable and should be investigated. Problems of this nature can usually be overcome with the use of voltage stabilisers.

Whilst the operating environment does not, therefore, present a problem in terms of atmospheric conditions, it is important to install the system in a physical location which is going to maximise its effective use. This will normally mean locating it within the design office itself and certainly not placing it in a separate room called the 'Computer Room'. It is also important that staff who are to use the computer are adequately prepared not only in the physical use of the machine and programs, but also in the office policy towards its use. At one extreme the computer housed in a separate room may rarely be used. On the other hand, if no guidance is given as to suitable types of application, it may become overused to the extent that trivial tasks are denying the processing of more appropriate work.

The organisation of the physical accessories should be carefully thought out. This includes arrangements for back-up copies of master discs and data discs (if necessary), the distribution of working discs, and the location of the documentation.

With a little careful preparation the system will enjoy a successful launch and, although there will inevitably be a period of familiarisation, this should ensure a continuing success.

10.5 Implications on professional integrity

One of the most disturbing aspects when considering any form of computer-aided design is the professional responsibility for design errors arising from the use of a program written by somebody else. The question, and the various arguments (often highly philosophical) arising from it, justify a separate book, but we conclude that it is a danger that must be accepted at the outset or the principle of computer-aided design rejected immediately.

Program errors can arise in a number of ways and for various reasons:

(a) Systems analysis errors
Such errors arise because of a fault in the program's concept of the analysis or design, the criteria used, and the way in which the program interprets or acts on results;

(b) Programming errors
Incorrect program coding resulting in the production of spurious results;

(c) User errors
The inappropriate use of a program, either in concept or using extreme combinations of data not originally conceived by the programmer, incorrect interpretation and unquestioned acceptance of results;

(d) Computer errors
Despite the excuses offered by embarrassed programmers, computer errors very rarely produce incorrect results. Computer errors result in a total failure of the system, from which results can rarely be obtained.

Systems analysis and programming errors do occur; it must be accepted that any but the most simple program is likely to contain inconsistencies which can be termed errors. While the partners of a consultancy practice may worry that errors could jeopardise their professional integrity, program authors are considerably more concerned because they know how easy it is for errors to lie dormant in a program, previously thought to have been fully tested. We believe that users of commercial software must suspect any program until their suspicions are proved unfounded, but that this should not mean a rejection of computer-aided design.

Incorrect results arising from user errors should be of considerably greater concern than program errors. The manual should clearly state the range of problems for which a program is valid: it is too easy for programs to be used by engineers having little knowledge or experience of the conventional design process, and for totally inappropriate problems to be applied to the program. We believe that the results of any program must be presented in such a way that they can be cross-checked against more conventional methods (often engineering judgement!) and show that they are internally consistent. For example, the results of a CP110 beam design should show the appropriate values of M/bd^2 for easy comparison with the standard design charts, or total forces on a frame member resolved and displayed to prove overall consistency.

Although of little consolation to the managers of any design office, we would suggest that control of the user is more important than questioning program validity. Too often we have heard anecdotes incorporating the phrase 'it must be right, the computer said so'; we suggest that the first responsibility of any manager is to accept the results of a computer only if the computer *and* the user say that it is right. To this end some programs display a message at the end of the program reminding the user that the responsibility for the results lies with him.

The foregoing can be summed up by emphasising that we are discussing computer-*aided* design, not *computerised* design. The minor difference in wording is not just a subtlety; it embraces the whole principle that the engineer is the designer and is being assisted by a computer as and when he considers appropriate. Most program suppliers will insist on a contract of sale absolving the supplier of any responsibility for errors or omissions in the program. We believe that this is a necessity, if only to emphasise to the purchaser at the outset that the final responsibility for a design lies with the engineer.

References

BCSA/Constrado (1978) *Structural Steelwork Handbook: properties and safe load tables*, BCSA, London, and Constrado, Croydon.

BS449 (1969) *The Use of Structural Steel in Building*, British Standards Institution, London.

Constrado (1972) *Steel Designer's Manual*, Crosby Lockwood Staples, London.

DOC (1980) *Micros in Construction*, Design Office Consortium, Cambridge.

Jackson, M. (1980) 'Design and use of conventional programming languages', Ch. 11, pp. 321–347 in Smith, H. T. and Green, T. G. R. (eds.), *Human Interaction with Computers*, Academic Press, London.

Sammet, J. E. (1976) 'Roster of programming languages for 1974–75', *Comm. ACM*, 19, 655–669.

Snaith, M. S., Burrow, J. C. and Orr, D. (1982) 'System BS. Highway pavement evaluation and management system for the assessment, design and treatment of flexible pavements', *Proceedings of the Seminar on Maintenance and Drainage Aspects of Road Pavements*, Bangalore, pp.121–129.

Terman, L. M. (1977) 'The role of microelectronics in data processing', *Scientific American*, 237, 162–177.

A Glossary of terms

Address	: The location of a specific part of memory.
Algorithm	: The method of solution of a problem stated as a logical computational procedure.
Applications program	: A program to perform a specific task for the user.
Array	: A set of individual variables with a common name each variable uniquely defined by a subscript.
ASCII	: American Standard Code for Information Interchange.
ASCII codes	: ASCII standarised numeric values for all characters used in a computer system.
Assembler	: A program which converts a programmer's mnemonic instructions into binary code for the specific microprocessor being used.
Assembly language	: A low-level mnemonic programming language specific to the microprocessor being used.
BASIC	: Beginners All-purpose Symbolic Instruction Code. A high-level interpreted or compiled programming language.
Batch processing	: Complete processing of a progam and data involving no interaction with program user.
Baud	: Data transmission rate over telephone networks or between computers and peripherals. Equal to one bit per second.
Binary	: A system of arithmetic to the base of two.
Bit	: Contraction of 'binary digit'. One bit is the smallest unit of data, taking a value of 0 or 1.
Boolean algebra	: The expression of logical as distinct from arithmetic relationships.

Booting the system	: Transferring the operating system from disc to the computer's memory.
Bug	: An endearing term for a program or system error.
Bureau service	: A commercial service offering the use of programs and/or computer time.
Bus	: A communication path between the different components of a computer.
Byte	: A group of eight bits (binary digits).
Chaining	: A method of automatically passing control from one program to another whilst retaining the values of specified variables.
Channel	: A means of identifying the communicating route to a disc file.
Check digit	: An additional digit or bit at the end of an item of data to verify that the data has been transmitted and interpreted correctly.
Chip	: See 'Integrated Circuit'.
Clock	: A signal generator transmitting a fixed frequency signal to synchronise computer operations.
Communications protocol	: The choice of a particular set of standards for data transmission rate, word length, check digits, etc. for communication between computers and/or peripherals.
Compiler	: A program which converts a source program written in a high-level language to machine-code for the particular microprocessor being used.
Configuration	: The physical components of a system. Sometimes refers to the communications protocol.
CP/M	: Control Program for Microcomputers. A proprietary Operating System developed by Digital Research Inc.
cps	: Characters per second – a measure of printing speed.
CPU	: Central Processing Unit. The central controller of a computer which operates the fetch-execute cycles and maintains the status of results of operations.
Cursor	: A flashing or static symbol used to identify a point on a visual display unit.

Database : A file of data organised in a consistent format which allows data to be entered, retrieved, updated and sorted.

Dedicated : A computer used by only one individual at a time for a single task.

Digitiser : A physical device for transferring co-ordinates from a drawing to a computer.

Disc-cache : Extra random access memory simulating an additional disc drive.

Execution : The processing of a program by a computer.

Fetch-execute cycle : The fundamental operation of the CPU controlled by the computer's clock.

Field : Part of a data record containing information in a predefined format.

File : An organisational method of recording information on disc or tape. Separate files can be created to contain separate programs or data.

Firmware : Programs permanently installed in integrated circuits in a computer.

Floppy disc : A thin magnetically-sensitive disc used for mass storage of information.

Flow chart : The diagrammatic representation of a program as a series of interrelated activities.

Format : The definition of the layout of information.

Formatting discs : The preparation of a floppy disc in terms of tracks and sectors in accordance with the specification for the particular microcomputer being used.

FORTRAN : Contraction of Formula Translation. A high-level compiled programming language used in scientific and engineering applications.

Free format : An undefined layout of information, usually in which data follows each other sequentially.

Graphics : The means of displaying pictorial information, rather than text, on the screen.

Graphics board : Additional memory enabling a microcomputer to produce graphics.

Graphics page : A method of reserving certain parts of memory for graphical display.

Hard copy	: Information, generally results, produced in printed form.
Hard disc	: High-capacity, high-speed, fixed disc mass storage, also known as a Winchester disc.
Hardware	: The physical components of a computer system.
High-level language	: A standardised programming language which is meaningful to a programmer and usually relatively independent of the computer being used.
Housekeeping	: The process of removing redundant information, making more internal or backing store memory available, etc.
HRG	: High resolution graphics – a system of graphics enabling the display of pictures of good definition on the screen.
Hung-up	: An apparent breakdown in the communication from the computer to the user, generally due to the program locking into an endless loop.
I/O	: Input/Output. The general term used for entering or receiving information.
Instruction	: A command to a microprocessor to carry out a standard operation contained in its instruction set.
Instruction set	: The set of commands which a microprocessor is capable of obeying.
Integrated circuit	: A circuit in which all electronic components have been permanently formed on a single piece of semiconductor material.
Intelligent terminal	: A computer terminal with its own processor capable of working independently or, if required, to use the resources of the host computer.
Interactive computing	: A method of computing in which the program user is able to control and influence the progress of program execution.
Interface	: A physical device to allow data to be transmitted and received between computers and peripheral equipment.
Internal memory	: The memory contained within the computer itself.
Interpreter	: A program which decodes a high-level programming language, one statement at a time, to instructions meaningful to a microprocessor.

Interpreted language	: A programming language capable of operation with an interpreter.
K or Kbytes	: Abbreviation for 1 024 (or 2^{10} bytes).
Key	: (a) Keyboard key.
	(b) An item of data in a database used for sorting records into the required order.
Listing	: The printing of information on a printer.
LRG	: Low resolution graphics – a system of graphics enabling the display of simple pictorial shapes only, usually composed of keyboard characters.
Machine code	: The binary instruction codes specific to the microprocessor being used.
Mainframe	: A large computer system using 32 or more bit words with large amounts of internal and backing store and capable of supporting a number of terminals and peripherals.
Mass storage	: A physical device using a magnetic medium to record permanently programs and data. Common types are cassette tapes and floppy discs.
Mbyte or Megabyte	: One million bytes.
Memory	: Integrated circuits capable of temporarily storing information.
Memory map	: A diagrammatic representation of the use of different parts of memory.
Memory size	: The total number of separate bytes that can be addressed.
Menu	: The display of a list of alternatives within a program, enabling the user to make a simple selection.
Microprocessor	: A single integrated circuit which performs the functions of the CPU.
Minicomputer	: The distinction between different types of computers is becoming very ill-defined, particularly with the evolution of 16-bit micros. A minicomputer is thus best defined as a computer which is bigger than a micro, but smaller than a mainframe!

Monitor : A television-like screen, but producing a display which is more stable and has better definition.

Monitor program : A firmware program which comes into operation as soon as the computer is switched on, often to carry out a memory check and to boot the system.

MSDOS : A proprietary Operating System for 16-bit micros.

Multi-user : The general description of a computer used by more than one user at any time.

Network : A system which allows a number of computers to communicate with each other and share common resources.

Non-volatile memory : Memory which retains information in the absence of electric power.

Number-crunching : The processing of lengthy, complex numerical calculations.

Off-line : Operations carried out independently of the CPU.

On-line : Operations carried out under the direct control of the CPU.

Operating System : A set of either firmware or software programs which control the resources of a computer, particularly application program control, mass store and peripherals.

Package : A general term for a number of interrelated programs.

Paging : (a) The control of printer paper to start at the 'top of the form'.

(b) The management of screen displays into a consistent form.

Parallel interface : A method of data transfer to and from peripherals in which data bits are transmitted along parallel wires.

Parity : A convention using a 'Parity Bit' so that the sum of all bits in a word or byte is always either odd or even.

Parity bit : An additional data bit causing the sum of all bits to match either odd or even parity.

Peripheral : Equipment which may be connected to and controlled by a computer.

Pixel : One small element of a high resolution graphics screen which may be illuminated.

Plotter : A device for producing drawings.

Port : A socket allowing connection of the computer to a peripheral device.

Post-processing : The processing of numerical results from a general purpose program, such as a finite element analysis, into a more convenient form.

Pre-processing : The processing of simple data into a form suitable for treatment by general purpose programs, such as finite element analysis.

Program : A sequence of instructions written in a particular programming language to be performed by a computer.

Programming language : A method of writing instructions to be performed by a computer.

Random access file : A system of backing store organisation which allows any one item of data to be accessed selectively and independently of all other data.

RAM or random access memory : Internal memory which can be accessed and changed by a program or by the user.

Real-time : The processing of data in response to events actually occurring at the current time. Used particularly in data logging, machine control, etc.

Record : A set of one or more fields of related data.

Register : A 'pigeon hole' within RAM in which one item of information can be stored.

Reserved words : Certain words which have a specific meaning in the programming language and which must not therefore be used as variable names.

Response time : The time between the last command from the user and the next response by the computer.

Resetting the system : Returning to the operating system.

ROM or read only memory : Internal memory which can be accessed by a program or user but whose values cannot be changed. PROM is non-volatile Read Only Memory which can be permanently programmed using special equipment, whilst EPROM can also be erased, again with special equipment.

Screen dump	: An exact copy of the screen display produced on a plotter or printer.
Sector	: A division on a floppy disc.
Serial interface	: A method of data transfer to and from peripherals in which data bits are transmitted sequentially along a single data path.
Sequential file	: A system of backing store organisation in which data is stored sequentially in free format. No single item of data can be accessed independently of preceding data.
Software	: A general name for computer programs.
Source	: The original (usually high-level language) program which requires either an interpreter or compiler before the instructions can be processed.
Speed	: A computer's speed is generally defined in terms of the number of fetch-execute cycles which can be performed in one second.
Subroutines	: A relatively independent part of a program performing a specific task but requiring the values of variables to be passed from the controlling program.
Subscript	: A number identifying a unique element of an array.
Syntax	: The 'grammatical' rules of a high-level language. A violation of these rules is referred to as a 'syntax error'.
Systems analysis	: The process of defining a problem in terms of logical procedures as a precursor to program writing.
Systems programs or software	: Machine-code programs run from the operating system.
Terminal	: A data entry and output device connected to a computer.
Track	: A division on a floppy disc.
Turnkey	: A complete hardware and software system offered by a supplier.
User	: The person using an application program.

User RAM	: The amount of random access memory available for an applications progam.
VDU	: Visual Display Unit – a cathode-ray tube type of display of input and output data. In some contexts this refers to an integral screen and keyboard, but has become more generally used for the screen of a microcomputer system. It is the latter meaning which has been used in this book.
Volatile memory	: Internal memory (Random Access Memory) whose content is lost in the absence of electric power.
Word-processing	: The manipulation of text displayed on the screen prior to printing.
Work file	: A temporary file created, typically on disc, to store intermediate results of a progam.

Index